W9-DIY-710

THADDEUS LOWE
AMERICA'S ONE-MAN AIR CORPS

"There is no curse upon man by which the realm of the air is forbidden to his travel. . ."
Anon.

Professor Lowe dictating dispatch during Battle of Fair Oaks, 1861. *Copy of wood print in Lowe Collection, Smithsonian Institution*

←

Elevating balloon "Intrepid" for aerial reconnaissance during Civil War. *Copy of photo in Lowe Collection, Smithsonian Institution*

Professor Lowe, in foreground, preparing telegraph to report aerial observation during Civil War. *Smithsonian Institution*

Thaddeus S. C. Lowe, during Civil War. *The National Archives*

←

Will Lieut Genl. Scott please see Professor Lowe, once more about his balloon?
A Lincoln
July 25, 1861

Note written by Abraham Lincoln: "Will Lieut Genl. Scott please see Professor Lowe, once more about his balloon. A. Lincoln, July 25, 1861."

First balloon ascension of Professor Lowe, July 17, 1858. *Copy of engraving, Lowe Collection, Smithsonian Institution*

←

Inflating balloon "Great Western" for trial ascent prior to start of transatlantic trip, Philadelphia, 1859. Professor Lowe, in foreground, wearing high silk hat. *Smithsonian Institution*

→

Boat, basket, etc. for transatlantic balloon project of Professor Lowe, 1859. *Smithsonian Institution*

←

THADDEUS LOWE

America's One-Man Air Corps

Born
August 20, 1832
Died
January 16, 1913

By *MARY HOEHLING*

JULIAN MESSNER, INC. • *New York*

Published by Julian Messner, Inc.
8 West 40 Street, New York 18

Published simultaneously in Canada
by The Copp Clark Publishing Co. Limited

Printed in the United States of America

Library of Congress Catalog Card No. 58-7260

TO CLARA . . . .

ACKNOWLEDGMENTS

I wish to express my appreciation to Professor Lowe's grandsons, Russell J. Brownback and John S. Haug, for their interest and aid in preparing this biography . . . .

to his nephew Vyron, son of Charles Edward, and to Mrs. J. Ernest Plaisted, Librarian at Jefferson, New Hampshire, and granddaughter of Moranda Hicks. They patiently searched their memories for details of Thad's early life, and generously shared mementoes of the Lowe family . . . .

to Elizabeth Brown, Librarian at the Aeronautics Institute, New York City . . . .

to Thomas Coulson, Director of Research at the Benjamin Franklin Institute, Philadelphia . . . .

to Paul Edward Garber, Head Curator of the National Air Museum of the Smithsonian Institute, Washington, D. C. . . . .

to Mildred P. McKay, New Hampshire State Librarian, and to Hugh Harvey of the Shell Oil Company . . . .

to the reference and research staffs and librarians of the Boston Public Library, the Harvard College Library, the Ferguson Library of Stamford, Connecticut, the Historical and Philosophical Society of Ohio, the Historical Society of Pennsylvania, and the New York Public Library . . . .

to my husband, for his able assistance, and to Barbara, Patsy, and Dolph who helped in countless ways.

CONTENTS

PROLOGUE

Within the past year, captive balloons have been used as launching platforms to send rockets into outer space.

In another Air Force experiment, Dr. David Simons was sent nineteen miles high in a giant balloon. He spent thirty-two hours in the balloon's tiny compartment, the longest period a man has ever spent in conditions approximating those of outer space.

These steps in the conquest of the universe really began over one hundred years ago, when the dreams of a New Hampshire scientist spanned time towards a generation not yet born . . . .

. . . . began with the story of Thaddeus Lowe.

CHAPTER ONE

WHITE MOUNTAIN BOY

It was dark when he awoke, and his nose was cold. Not a ray of sun had topped the snowy peaks to the east of Jefferson Mills, New Hampshire. But from sounds beneath his loft room, Thaddeus Lowe could tell that it was morning.

He pulled the covers over his nose. Half awake, he tried to ignore the younger children running about the kitchen. The splat-splat of their bare feet on bare pine boards drummed through the frame house.

The smell of porridge cooking on the wood stove drifted up to him. He pictured his stepmother, Mary Randall, wrapped in her heavy quilted robe, stirring it with a great wooden spoon.

The bang of the woodshed door prodded Thad into acute wakefulness. The heavy tread of booted feet followed by a rolling thud announced his father's entrance with a load of kindling.

It must be past six! He should be over at the Plaisted's now, helping with the livestock.

Then he remembered school.

He let out a warwhoop and jumped up. Running to the washstand, Thad doused himself with the icy water that had stood in the china pitcher all night. Clean clothes hanging stiff over the back of his only chair confirmed his joy.

Today was the day—December 1st, 1842—the day he

returned to Common School at Jefferson Hills for another three months!

Spurred by excitement as well as cold, Thad was dressed in seconds. The sound of men's voices below his window told him it was nearly seven, the time when work started at the lumber mill near his father's store.

Thad's long body catapulted down the steep stair. He found his father and stepmother laughing at him, his four stepbrothers and sisters staring at his antics.

"Take it easy, boy," his father said. "You don't have to be up to the school till 8:30. With those legs you should cover the two miles like you had seven-league boots."

"There is one thing you forgot in your haste, Thad." His stepmother's voice was quiet, but in five years Thad had learned to pay attention. His father, Clovis Lowe, had married Mary Randall the same year Thad started school. He had no clear memories before that, not even of his own mother.

Now Mary Randall was looking at his hair. Running his fingers self-consciously through the wet, black mass, he excused himself and climbed back to his room.

As Thad reached the top of the ladder, he heard Mary's voice above the baby's gurgles. "The boy ought to have a chance at more schooling. Curious about everything, just like you, Clovis."

"All in good time, Mary," Clovis replied. "Thad's only ten. He's got his mother's strong will—not easygoin' like me."

Clovis Lowe would never be wealthy. Everyone in the valley traded at his store but it was not in him to dun a man for a bill or let any family go without necessities. Yet he was well traveled and well read. He had served as selectman and delegate to the state legislature. His opinion was respected throughout the county.

"He may have his ma's strong will, but, thank goodness, he inherited your good nature, Clovis."

"He'll use the determination for something worthwhile, I'll warrant," Clovis replied. "Soon enough he'll grow too big for Jefferson, like Joseph did."

Thad's fourteen-year-old brother Joseph had left for Boston only the past summer to learn the trade of boot- and shoe-cutting.

"There's something special about Thad though," Mary Randall said thoughtfully. "Thaddeus Sobieski Constantine Lowe. It's as if Alpha Green put all her dreams into her son's name. It's a name to carry like a banner. . . . I have a feeling the boy's going to live up to it."

The road Thad walked toward Jefferson Hills wound through a fertile valley now winter frozen. The Pliny Range walled the valley on his left. Cherry Mountain, to his right, was topped by a bald spur called Owl's Head.

Behind Cherry Mountain towered the Waumbek-Methna —the "Mountains with snowy foreheads" the Indians called them. From Crawford Notch they swept back towards the town of Randolph, enclosing the valley on his left. This was the Presidential Range: Washington, Adams, Madison . . .

To have a mountain named for him seemed to Thad the highest tribute a man could ask. He loved the mountains though he often felt they were imprisoning him in his valley home.

It was true he could not learn fast enough, could never find enough to read. The Coos County schools provided no books. His father supplied him as best he could and his teacher often lent Thad those from his own library. Both men encouraged the boy, tried to answer his questions. Still his mind reached out for more. . . .

Topping a knoll, the familiar buildings of Jefferson Hills intruded on Thad's reverie. His father had been right. His long, sturdy legs had carried him the two miles in no time. He was still early.

Down to his right, almost at the foot of Cherry Mountain, lay Cherry Pond, glistening in the frost. In spring the boys would sneak away from the plowing for a day of fishing there. It was worth the caning they might receive, for the pond was alive with speckled trout. Usually the boys would bring a string of the beauties home for supper. Then what mother could be angry?

Above the pond toward the village, on a rise called Indian Hill, dwelt pitiful remnants of a proud tribe, an offshoot of the Algonquins. Smoke from the Red Men's breakfast fires was rising from the rounded tepees. Thad decided to say hello to his friends.

As he approached the wigwam village, several boys his age ran out to greet him. Today they would hunt with their fathers in the mountains, bring back buck for food and clothing. If he stopped on the way home, perhaps they would have one to show him!

Thaddeus had grown up with the Indians and learned to admire them though many of the Puritan settlers considered them lazy. In spare time squeezed between school and chores, Thad had learned their crafts. They taught him to weave stiff straw into beautiful baskets, to make dishes from the soft river clay, to sew heavy deer hides into moccasins, and work into them handsome bead decorations.

He had even made his own bow and arrows, molding the wood and inserting the feathers at one end so they would fly true. At ten he was more skilful with his hands than any white boy in the county, making him much in demand throughout the valley for intricate tasks about farm or house.

Now the Chief greeted him cordially. "Snow on Agiochook"; he said, waving toward Washington, "on Ammonoosuk, Mooshillock, Contoocook, Pentucket." The Chief's hand swept the Presidential Range, giving the mountains their Algonquin names. "Season good for buck. We go find."

Then he raised both hands toward Thaddeus. "Tall white boy, you hunt with us one day. Find food for your family, make nice skirt or slippers for Mama and baby sisters."

Thad had never before been invited to hunt with the Indians. It meant not only that the old patriarch had accepted him as an adopted son, an honor in itself, but also that they considered him manly—ready to learn the arts of man's estate.

Thad continued the short distance to school in even higher spirits than before. "Someday," he thought, looking up at the mountains surrounding him, "someday I shall fly right over those mountains!" Then he laughed at the boldness of his own dreams.

The following Saturday, Clovis let Thaddeus hunt with the Indians. With bow and arrow he sped across the wooded slope of Cherry Mountain as silently as any of them. As the lowering sun glanced off Owl's Head, Thad and a small group came out on a clearing. There, against a jut of rock opposite them, a stag stood spotlighted in the sun's rays.

Thaddeus had reached the clearing first. The Indians stood silently in the tree shadows as he raised his bow and took aim. The arrow sped across the narrow gorge. The stag reared as the arrow pierced the shaggy fur of his neck.

Then, as he wheeled to flee, the Indians loosed a flight of arrows that felled him. But it was Thad's buck.

During the next weeks, Thad spent many afternoons with the Indians. The rich venison steaks he brought home were tastier because liberally spiced with pride. That Christmas his whole family had handwrought moccasins, and for his stepmother, Thad made a pouch to carry thread and other household oddments.

In the winter evenings, the family sang hymns after supper. The strains of their off-tune efforts rang through the house fervently.

> When marshalled on the midnight plains,
> The heavenly host appears . . .

While Mary Randall tucked the baby into bed, Thad would sometimes linger to hear part of the bedtime story read by Moranda Hicks, a neighbor's daughter who "helped out." But by 7:30 he was always deep in his own books.

Thad would lie on his stomach before the pine knot fire while Clovis worked at his cobbler's bench nearby, for he was the village shoemaker too. When Thad finished his assigned work, he would read aloud to his father or they just talked.

Mary Randall's golden head would nod over her quilting as their voices lulled her. Only when the pine knots simmered so low that the chill made further work or reading unbearable, would they go off to bed.

On August 20th, 1843, Thaddeus celebrated his eleventh birthday. That year was marked in Thad's memory because his family moved to a larger home in Jefferson Hills, directly opposite the Starr King school. Although Thad had been born in the yellow frame house at the Mills, he left it with little regret. The move meant he could attend the short midsummer session of school.

Whenever he could, Thaddeus helped his father in the store. He liked particularly to be there toward the end of the day, when the men came in from work. Winter evenings they would gather around the wood stove to read the papers and discuss the day's events.

On Monday, April 15th, 1844, Thad was the first to see Saturday's *New York Sun,* when it arrived in Jefferson with:

ASTOUNDING NEWS!
ATLANTIC CROSSED IN THREE DAYS!
SIGNAL TRIUMPH OF MR. MONCK MASON'S
FLYING MACHINE!

The story described how the "Steering Balloon, *Victoria*" had flown from North Wales to Charleston, S. C., in 75 hours with eight men aboard.

The news was all over Jefferson in a few hours. The store became a hubbub of loud and varied opinions.

"Two of those fellers—that Monck Mason and Robert Hollond were with Charles Green when he ballooned from London to Germany way back in 1836," remarked Clovis Lowe. "If they could do that then, this don't seem so unlikely."

"Oh, but the Atlantic Ocean's a lot wider'n that there English Channel," one countryman observed, and the discussion was on again.

Thaddeus knew that man had ventured aloft with some success since 1783. The great Benjamin Franklin himself had witnessed the ascension of the first Montgolfiere balloon at Annonay, France, on June 5th of that year, and described the event in his journal. On September 19th of the same year, Franklin had watched animals—a chicken, a duck, and a sheep—carried harmlessly aloft.

Many an evening, as Thad lay before the fire, he imagined himself sharing the Montgolfiere brothers' first experiments with smoke from their fireplace and a tiny homemade bag. He had followed them through trial and error until that great day in November, 1783, when one of their balloons carried human beings aloft for the first time in history.

Propelled by hot air from a wool and straw fire, the gaily decorated Montgolfiere bore two young noblemen 300 feet over Paris, where the brave volunteers saluted the awe-struck crowd below. Then a southerly wind carried them five miles in twenty minutes, landing them safely in a field. The aspirations of 5000 years were realized.

Man had flown!

He knew, too, that within five years of that first flight, "flammable air" or hydrogen replaced hot air as a lifting agent. Ballooning became such a fad that even women trusted themselves aloft in the fascinating new toy.

And not all were flying purely for sport. Scientists such as Dr. John Jeffries of Boston and the noted French aeronaut, Jean-Pierre Blanchard risked their lives repeatedly to learn more about upper air currents and their role in aeronautics.

On a bitter January day in 1787, they had been forced to throw everything out of their balloon including their own clothing in order to soar over the cliffs of France. The first flight across the English channel, from Dover to Calais, had been successfully concluded by the two balloonists—in their underwear!

Now, if men had flown the Atlantic Ocean, the air was indeed conquered. What was left for a man to do?

Two days later the *Sun* reported: "The mails from the South last Saturday night not having brought confirmation of the arrival of the balloon from England, we are inclined to believe the intelligence is erroneous."

The story proved a gigantic hoax. An impoverished writer named Edgar Allan Poe had arrived in New York the preceding week. His wife was sick, he counted only $4.50 in his pocket. The wild tale was a desperate attempt to make money. What newsmen called "balloonantics" had been royally spoofed and everyone had a good laugh—everyone, that is, except young Thaddeus Lowe.

CHAPTER TWO

FLYING TOMCAT

Thad's bare feet kicked up a cloud of August dust as his long legs reached out across the 80 miles to Portland. His black hair was matted from the heat and gray with grime. But his carpet bag, strapped across his shoulders, bounced merrily as he walked. He was fifteen years old this very month, and off on his own.

Secured tightly round his waist, well hidden beneath his flapping shirt, was a fat billfold. It contained over $100! He had been saving for this day since he was twelve.

He had never had trouble finding jobs. Despite his unusual height and apparent ungainliness, Thad still moved with the fleet grace of an Indian. There was no quicker, harder worker in the valley, and, at twelve, he had already gained the reputation of being a "shrewd" lad.

Nothing escaped his consuming curiosity—the biological functions of the animals, the weather and its effect on the crops, the chemistry of the soil. His teacher at the Common School had found it necessary to map out a special course of study for him, emphasizing Botany, Geology, Mechanics, and Chemistry.

Rumblings of war in Mexico had reached Jefferson in the spring of 1845. During the second year of the war, the papers carried a story that made Thad prick up his ears. John Wise, America's leading aeronaut, proposed to break the deadlock at Vera Cruz by bombing San Juan Castle from the air.

Wise claimed he could carry an 18,000-pound load of "percussion bombshells and torpedoes," in a balloon which was to be maneuvered into position on a cable.

The government never took Wise's proposition seriously. It was ridiculed by all but a few forward looking newspapers such as the Philadelphia *Public Ledger,* which said, "the plan should be given a try!"

Thaddeus had agreed.

His teacher shook his head over the idea. "Likely as not the balloon, crew and all, would be blown to kingdom come along with the target," the schoolmaster surmised. "Yet, balloons have been used successfully in war."

Next day he lent Thad a learned volume on the Napoleonic campaigns. Napoleon Bonaparte had been a dreamer as well as a master strategist. As early as 1794, he had recognized the possibilities of aerostation in battle and formed an air corps as soon as he could get dependable balloons.

In his imagination, Thaddeus had floated right out over enemy lines with the "Captain of Aerostiers," J. M. J. Coutelle.

"He must have felt like God," Thad told his teacher. "He could see what was going to happen before it did and warn the troops below. He spotted for the artillery too. Why, they were able to hit targets they couldn't even see!"

Thad had given the military uses of aircraft deep thought. "Battles could be shortened and hundreds of lives might be saved if the enemy's movements were known in advance."

"Never mind, Thad," his teacher reassured him. "We'll win the war, anyway. And we'll take San Juan without Wise's help."

"Yes," Thad had answered slowly, "but think of all the American soldiers that will be killed storming the castle."

As Thaddeus went into his fifteenth summer, his father

had decided another move would be necessary to accommodate the yearly increase in his family. Clovis had his eye on a large farm in the neighboring town of Randolph, his birthplace, where he thought of opening a guest house and guide service.

Thad had listened to his father's plans silently, knowing the time had come for him to make a break. Looking around the crowded supper table in the spotless gay kitchen, he realized that leaving would not be easy. He pushed back his chair with a jerk.

"You know, Pa . . ." he began.

"Yes, Thad, I know." Clovis sighed. "I'll write your brother, down to Boston. He'll help you get started in a trade. After that it's up to you. But never forget, son, this is your home."

Thad's friends at the mill, where he'd done odd jobs, arranged for him to take a sailor's berth aboard a coastal lumber schooner, and by the middle of August he was on his way to meet the ship.

Walking from Jefferson to Portland proved an easy trip. Farmers gave him rides, sometimes fed him, even let him sleep in their barns in return for a few chores. On clear nights he preferred to lie under the stars, counting them before he dropped off to sleep, jealously, as if they were pieces of his new-found freedom.

The seaport was huge. Buildings four stories high stood in lines leading down to the wharves. The constant clatter and bustle was exciting, even frightening to a mountain boy. Cart horses drew wagons over the rutted streets at such a clip that it seemed to Thad worth a man's life to venture out on foot.

An alien smell filled the dusty air. As Thad approached the wharves it became so strong it made his nose wrinkle.

He thought it was the sea until his boat carried him away from land and he realized it had been a special wharf odor. Salt air, yes, but mixed with drying fish, leather, tar, and the thousand other odors emanating from as many cargoes fetched from every corner of the earth.

The first night aboard ship the constant creaking and groaning of the rigging and the old hull, the sudden radical changes of angle called "tacking," kept waking Thad up. But soon the boat's motion became soothing. The pungent scent of the newly cut lumber made him feel at home and the scurrying rats amused him. He confided to one surprised sailor that if he had not already decided to be a balloonist he might have considered the sea.

If Portland had seemed large, Boston, center of the world trade and New England fishing, was overwhelming. The wharf noises and smells were appalling. Thad's brother led him through winding streets where dark buildings and warehouses crowded down on them. Thad shivered in the early morning chill, wondering if the sun ever reached these manmade caverns.

They emerged suddenly on an immense park Joseph said was the Common. Above them rose a hill with square brick houses marching neatly up it and topped by the State House, its yellow dome gleaming in the morning sun.

"I've got to get back to my shoe shop in Chelsea," Joseph was saying, "but I thought you'd like to see some of the sights before you go down the south shore to Hingham."

"You've apprenticed me to Mr. Nash then, the man who taught you shoemaking?" Thad was disappointed that he was not to be in the city. Evidently his voice showed it, for Joseph replied impatiently.

"Look here, young one. I know you've got big ideas, but

you've got to start somewhere. Nash, French, and Co. are the best boot and shoe manufacturers in this part of the country—and no boy could ask for a fairer, kinder patron than Mr. William Otis Nash!"

Mr. Nash noticed at once his new apprentice's eagerness to learn and his facility with his hands. Thad had been working in the shop only two months when he was given a task that had proved difficult for the most seasoned shoe cutters—the making of a congress boot.

A congress boot had a U-shaped opening on each side. Experts had been unsuccessful in making neat cutouts in the tough leather. The first one Thad made was perfect. Curious as to how he had done it, Mr. Nash and his foreman surreptitiously watched Thad as he cut the openings. They were amazed to see him lick the knife as he worked.

"The Indians always licked the knife when cutting hides," Thad explained. "I figured it would probably make a neater cut in shoe leather too."

A bowl of water was provided congress boot cutters after that.

Impressed with the activity of the boy's mind, Mr. Nash arranged Thad's schedule so he could continue his scientific studies. He even winked at what many masters would have considered madcap experiments, ingenious schemes that captured the imaginations of every young male in Hingham.

Spring brought an inevitable preoccupation with kite-flying, and Thad swiftly mastered the art. He became determined to build a monster kite which could carry an animal aloft, to test its reaction to altitude. He persuaded a boy named Willie to lend him his small dog, Bozo, for the experiment.

On the night of the trial flight Willie backed out, fearing for the safety of his pet.

"But Bozo'd make history," Thad pleaded. "He'd be the first flying dog!" But to no avail.

Thad's feet dragged as he walked back towards the group of waiting boys.

"Where's Bozo—and Willie? What's wrong, Thad?" The boys crowded around him.

Thad was angry, yet he could not bring himself to subject Willie to the cruel justice of the gang. He bit his lip and lied:

"Bozo's lost, and—Willie's family have work for him to do."

"What're you goin' to do? Does that mean the show's off?"

Thad kicked the pebbled road. Groping in his pockets, his fingers closed on the keys to Mr. Nash's store. He always kept the keys as he opened the shop in the morning and closed up at night.

What about the big black tomcat that lived in the shop? It wouldn't be exactly right to take the cat without permission. On the other hand he'd put him right back. So great was Thad's confidence in his invention, it never occurred to him that anything could go wrong.

Stealing the tom lent spice to the evening's activities. He was a huge, wild feline kept to discourage the rats attracted by the fragrant leather sides. But Thad had a way with animals and had little trouble coaxing him into the wire cage. Thad also "borrowed" the watchman's large glass lantern. It would make an excellent marker to show the kite's position when in the air.

The spot chosen for the experiment was an athletic field east of Hingham Centre where no trees or buildings could snag the kite. It was past ten when the boys trotted through the town with their booty. They met no one.

Thad pasted red tissue over one half of the lantern and tied it midway up the kite's tail. The cage containing the shivering cat was secured firmly at the end. Satisfied with his arrangements, Thad said, "Let's go."

As the boys paid out the line, a strong sea breeze from Cohasset caught the kite, blowing it back over the town. The boys had all they could do to hang on.

Thad had marked the rope so he could tell how far aloft the kite flew. When it reached 1000 feet, all hands were sore from holding the tugging monster and Thad told them to tie it to a hitching post at the edge of the field. Then they toured the town, viewing their handiwork from every angle. The big lantern, showing red and white as it twisted in the wind, made a very satisfactory marker.

At midnight they pulled the kite down. The lantern still glowed warmly, but the tom was a crouching ball of black fur that never moved. Only staring green eyes proved him still alive.

"That cat's scared most to death," observed one of the boys.

"I'll just stroke him a bit and he'll be all right," said Thad, starting to open the cage.

"Gee, I wouldn't put my hand in there for anything!"

Heeding the warning, Thad gingerly released the catch on the wire opening. A black streak whizzed past his ear and disappeared into the night. It was a mystery for days what had happened to old Tom. When he did appear back at the shop, he seemed to Thad's guilty eyes to have shrunk in size and fierceness.

On his way home that night, Thad vowed he would never frighten an innocent animal again. He would use flags or lanterns in his experiments—until he could go aloft himself.

"That cat is surely through with me," he thought sadly. "He has trusted me for the last time."

Next morning at breakfast, Mr. Nash was reading the paper when he suddenly broke his customary silence.

"That's odd," he said thoughtfully.

"What's odd, dear?" Mrs. Nash asked.

"Here's a report of an 'unusual changeable light' seen over Hingham Centre last night. About midnight it disappeared. Now, what could that have been? Eh, Thad, how about that? You're the scientist."

"I'm sure I can't understand it, sir," replied Thad innocently.

The subject was dropped. But Thad thought Mr. Nash was grinning to himself as he raised the paper and went back to his reading.

CHAPTER THREE

FLOATING SOAP BUBBLES

Charles Edward Lowe burst into his stepbrother's room in the farmhouse in Randolph one September afternoon in 1850. "Ma says you can take me over to the magic show at the town hall tonight if you feel like it. You want to go, don't you, Thad?"

Thad had been back in Randolph for several months. After two happy years with the Nashes he had gone into the shoe business with Joseph. But in the spring of 1850, a serious illness forced him to return home.

Sometimes, during the long summer, it had seemed to Thad he never would get well. Now, as he stood at his open window, the crisp pine-scented air awoke in him the old restlessness. Autumn foliage lit here and there the dark green firs that covered the mountain slopes.

"Knowledge is like those brilliant leaves," Thad thought, "lighting everyday life with bright sparks of new ideas."

Thad's intellectual hunger had returned full force with his body's strength. He had saved a good deal of his money in the past three years—not enough to go to a regular college, but he did want to use it for more education, somehow. . . . His brother's headlong entrance was a welcome relief from his confused thoughts.

The younger boy was waving a handbill. "See—it says here: 'PROFESSOR REGINALD B. DINCKLEHOFF,

WORLD RENOWNED CHEMIST, REVEALS WONDERS OF SCIENCE!' You wouldn't miss that, would you, Thad?"

"Sure wouldn't, Charlie." Thad ruffled the twelve-year-old's hair affectionately. "It'll be good to get out. Tell Ma I'll be right down to supper." Reluctantly he closed the window against the mountain air which became frigid the moment the sun disappeared behind the western peaks.

Later, Thad gave his own impromptu lecture on the stars and constellations as the two boys bounced along toward town in the farm rig.

Charlie was impressed. "Gee, Thad, you know more'n our teacher. Bet you know more'n anyone about astronomy and stuff!"

"Not yet, Charlie. But I sure hope to one of these days."

A crowd had turned out for the show. Before the curtain rose Thad encountered several schoolmates and neighbors from Jefferson whom he had not seen since his return. Attractive young women startled him by bowing coyly, until he remembered they must have been gawky pigtailed girls when last he saw them. Now, many were married and had growing families. The boys were equally unrecognizable. They had grown full beards and spoke in deep voices.

They, in turn, saw a Thaddeus grown even taller than they remembered, but no stringbean despite his six feet, two inches. He was broadshouldered and muscular, his handsome face unblemished. Its white, almost pallid skin was set off by jet black hair and a luxuriant auburn mustache.

Everyone greeted him warmly.

"Good to see you back, Thad."

"Sorry you've been ailin'."

Charlie led Thad to the front of the auditorium. They

had just settled down, when someone slipped into the seat beside Thad.

"Might have known you'd be here. Curious as ever, eh?" Thad turned to see his teacher, smiling, beside him.

Professor Dincklehoff now appeared before the curtain and his stentorian voice made further conversation impossible.

". . . but I propose to show you more than mere tricks of legerdemain," the portly showman was bellowing. "I propose to reveal to you—here tonight—in this town of Randolph, New Hampshire—wonders of the secret world of chemistry never before seen by any audience in the world!

"And now, if I could have a volunteer from the floor to assist me, please—"

Thad's schoolmaster and Charlie nudged him.

"Go on!" they whispered simultaneously. Thad was onstage in a minute.

It was a simple show, but the professor had to return for several bows after his closing address.

"How old are you, lad?" he asked Thad when he finally came backstage.

"Eighteen, sir."

Dincklehoff studied Thad carefully. "There's an alert and questioning mind behind those blue eyes," he thought.

"Most boys don't catch on to my routine as quickly as you," he told Thad. "Seemed like you knew what you were doing. Studied some science, have you?"

"Oh, yes sir," Thad replied. "Not just in school. I've read a lot on my own—and made some experiments."

"Well now, that's very interesting. Good to see a lad with curiosity about the wonders of science. Perhaps you'd like to assist me the rest of the week, eh? Can't pay much—harrumph. But you might learn a little something, eh?"

Seeing Thad's expression of pleasure, he added, "You can go right to work—get set up for tomorrow!"

At the end of the week Thad moved on with the show.

Two years later the aging Professor went into well earned retirement and with his savings Thad bought out the show.

The gruff showman had taught Thad a great deal. He had learned how to capture an audience, how to present a difficult subject simply enough to hold the attention of the dullest yokel. Best of all he had absorbed basic facts of chemistry and methods of test-tube experimentation.

Thad donned the traditional frock coat and top hat of the traveling showman, and officially adopted the title, "Professor of Chemistry." He kept his own name except for the substitution of the exotic sounding "Coulincourt" in place of Constantine. With his savings he added a portable laboratory to the show's equipment. At last, he could experiment with gasses, while also earning the money to make his dream come true. The self-taught cobbler's son had passed one milestone on the difficult road to becoming an aeronaut.

Thad's lectures drew record crowds. Though he emphasized increasingly the instructive part of the show, the legerdemain and magic tricks were hardly missed because Thad demonstrated simple facts of chemistry with a fine sense of showmanship.

"Observe these soapbubbles," he would cry as he and his assistant blew till they filled the room with them. "How airy and dainty they are!"

The audience watched the dancing globules as if mesmerized.

"Yes, airy and dainty. Apparently there is nothing but dew and imagination to hold together so ephemeral a creation. Yet see how the delicate envelope pulls the globe downward!"

Indeed the cloud of bubbles sank slowly but surely to the floor, as hundreds of eyes watched their inevitable progress earthward.

"Now there is nothing remarkable about the fact that a soapbubble cannot be supported in the air. The small amount of water and soap is still heavier than the atmosphere.

"But if you return tomorrow night, I propose to show you a phenomenon! A bubble that does float—right up to the ceiling—and will not come down!"

Few of his audience stayed home the next evening. They returned, bringing family and friends to witness the "phenomenon."

It was a simple trick but effective. Thad impregnated the bubbles with hydrogen, lightest of all the elements, which he produced by placing metal filings in a solution of sulphuric acid.

As the money flowed in, Thad increased his equipment. In the second year of his tour, he was able to buy several small balloons for a very special experiment.

As a boy he had often lain on his back in a field and watched the clouds go by. It appeared to Thad that the higher clouds traveled in one direction, eastward, even when the lower ones sped the opposite way.

He found that by reducing or increasing the amount of hydrogen and ballast in each tiny balloon he could regulate the height at which it would stop rising and move horizontally. By a thinner or thicker coat of varnish he could control the rate at which the gas disseminated, thus determining the length of time the balloons would remain in the air.

Imagine the delight of his spectators when he released a bunch of gaily colored balloons, saying, "The red ones will fly high and east, the yellow, low and west," and most of them did approximately that. Then Thad would disperse a group of lads to fetch them, telling them almost the exact spot where each would be found.

Thaddeus became convinced that the sky currents were as constant as rivers. Sometimes they were wide, sometimes narrow, sometimes their position varied by a quarter mile or so. One would have to follow them.

"In order to use the currents effectively," Thad told Joseph and Mr. Nash one evening when dining with them in Boston, "you would have to have a gadget to raise or lower the balloon without valving precious gas or tossing ballast. That way the aeronaut could find the needed current. It's the only rational way to traverse the air! And the only proper method of studying meteorology is from up there—in the air."

Joseph and Mr. Nash agreed that Thad was the man to invent that gadget. Nor were they alone in their admiration for his work. Schools and clubs invited him to give educational talks. His traveling laboratory bore little resemblance to the itinerant show he had joined back in 1850.

February 14th, 1855 found Thad in New York, engaged to lecture before the largest and most sophisticated audience he had yet faced. Lodging had been provided at a large, luxurious hotel.

The barefoot boy from Jefferson had acquired a poised and cultured manner equal to the situation. His handsome figure caused a rustle as he entered the gilded ballroom where he was to speak. There was no other sound but the tinkling of a million cutglass droplets in the huge chandeliers. Heavy brocade drapes shrouded the windows, keeping out the sounds of traffic—and the air.

Thad's nostrils were assailed by the overwhelming essence of a hundred mingled perfumes. He could not lecture effectively when he was smothering to death! He stepped from the platform and drew the draperies aside from the nearest window. Then he unbolted the sash and threw it wide to the February night. It meant his voice must compete with clopping hooves, squeaking carriage wheels, and the shouts of teamsters, but at least he could breathe.

As he walked back to the dais, he noted the well-bred faces of his audience register shock, amazement, some curiosity, even hostility. Many of the ladies ostentatiously drew their furs around them, shivering and whispering among themselves.

Thad immediately launched into an impromptu lecture on oxygen. Within minutes his audience was charmed. Forgotten was their distrust of fresh night air. They were certain this unique approach was part of his act.

Thad had trained himself to allow his eyes to sweep the audience when he spoke, apparently embracing all, resting on no one face. But as tonight's lecture progressed he found his attention straying persistently to a tiny figure in the first row.

The magnetic object appeared to be an exquisitely dressed doll. Everything about her was small. Her fashionable high-heeled shoes barely touched the floor. But her quick black eyes followed his every motion, her piquant face beneath an absurd feather hat registered flattering absorption in his every word.

By the end of the lecture Thad was completely fuddled and irritated with himself for not keeping his attention on his subject. Apparently his audience was not aware of his problem, for he was surrounded with the usual group of eager questioners. Yet his eyes still wandered over their heads.

"Looking for someone?" Thad turned to see a young reporter with whom he had become friendly.

"As a matter of fact, yes," Thad replied. "Can you wait a moment?"

When the crowd had dispersed and the equipment was being put away for the next night, Thad asked the newsman if he were acquainted with the tiny young woman who had been sitting in the front row.

"Indeed, yes," was the reply, "she's a French refugee, Leontine Gaschon. Her father was a palace guard for Louis Philippe, the so-called 'Citizen King.' You may remember the citizens decided he was acting too much like his uncle, Louis XVI, and revolted in February, 1848. The Gaschons escaped with the royal entourage out the back door of the Tuilleries as the Republicans entered the front. Leontine was just twelve years old at the time.

"Papa Gaschon, a Republican himself, left Louis Philippe in London and brought his family here. There's quite a colony of French expatriots in New York," the reporter pointed out.

"Leontine's made something of a name for herself as an actress, though she's only nineteen. She has a mind like a stropped razor and is very much interested in science. Want to meet her?"

Thad assented eagerly. As the two men made their way toward the lobby, the reporter chatted on:

"Leontine's an independent girl. She was educated like a princess, you know. It took a lot of spunk to get out and earn a living when she was trained for such a different life."

They found the Gaschons seated in the lobby and Thaddeus invited them all to late supper with him. Mama and Papa knew little English, but Leontine made up for their silence, her conversation not at all hampered by a charming accent. Her questions about Thad's work showed intelligent comprehension of the sciences.

Thad himself never knew how he answered. All through the meal he kept thinking, "How lovely she is," and, "What a coincidence that this is St. Valentine's Day." He needed no formula to prove he was in love.

Thad courted Leontine with the same singlemindedness with which he pursued knowledge. He was scheduled to remain in New York only one week before continuing his tour through the south. Never had he felt such a sense of urgency. He would not leave without her.

Seven days after their meeting, the big New Hampshire scientist and his tiny French bride stood before a Justice of the Peace in the hotel's oppressive Victorian salon and vowed to cherish one another until death.

Madame Gaschon wept happily into the champagne that the hotel manager had provided for all. It was a gay affair, but Thaddeus was silent, hardly believing his good fortune. He held Leontine's small hand so tightly she protested.

"*Mon cher marié, tu me blesse*—you hurt me." But she looked pleased.

Thad's eyes never left her lovely, laughing face. Surely finding his precious Leontine was the best thing that ever had or ever would happen to him.

Months later Leontine confessed to having shared that feeling. But it was years before she dared tell him that she herself had given fate a push. Her very good friend from the *Times* had been only too happy to arrange a meeting with the *"élégant, intélligent Professeur."*

CHAPTER FOUR

SHIPS OF THE AIR

Two years matured first love into an enduring affection —two years in which Thad discovered his beloved wife was also his most intelligent companion and willing helpmate, an enthusiastic sharer of his dreams.

Together they pored over balloon patterns spread out on the kitchen table of their small rented house in New York City. Together they deciphered the instructions in John Wise's book, *A System of Aeronautics:* how to cut the balloon cloth economically so no precious material would be wasted; how to sew strong seams; how to make a leak-proof valve. Leontine had insisted that every extra penny from the lecture tour go towards the construction of Thad's first aerostat.

The expected arrival of their first child prevented Leontine from visiting the construction site in Hoboken, on property leased from Mr. Stevens, a patron of the sciences. But she followed mentally every step of the building.

It was an April evening in 1857 when Thad announced the ship completed.

"The last coat of varnish was applied today," Thad cried as he burst into the tiny kitchen where Leontine was stirring soup over a wood stove. "Tomorrow, weather permitting, I will make my first ascension!"

"So it is completed," Leontine murmured. Apprehension gripped her as she realized the airship was a reality, that now Thad woull actually venture into a frightening new realm. . . .

"Are you all right, Leontine?" Thad asked anxiously as she placed his soup before him.

"It is this balloon, Thaddeus. I am suddenly afraid for you. You are sure it will ascend—that it will stay up in the air as it should? After all, you have never made one before."

Thad jumped up from the table and put his arms around her. "This is not my Leontine speaking." His lips brushed her soft hair. Then he held her from him, studying her troubled face. "You know I have seen to every stitch of the work myself. We followed the directions and patterns exactly. Of course, I have thought of ways to improve on Mr. Wise's methods. Why, my darling, this is only the beginning!"

Leontine took a deep breath. "Perhaps the baby coming makes me timid. Sit down and eat your supper while it's hot." Then, as she drew up her chair opposite him, "May I see your first ascension?"

The balloon was made of the finest twilled muslin. Thad pointed out each detail with pride.

It was a still, clear day and the aerostat was outside its shed being inflated from a nearby gas main. It was already tugging at its ropes. Thad stepped into the basket, while his crew, three farmhands who worked for Mr. Stevens, began to remove the sandbags attached to the rigging.

Soon the balloon floated easily just above the ground, held only by the crew. It was being tried for lift. Thad straightened and waved to Leontine, who returned his salute, heart in mouth.

She watched Thad toss out three or four more bags of

ballast. Then he reached up and broke the neck of the bag, which had been tied during inflation.

It made a loud noise, and the smell of coal gas filled the air. Leontine had to cover her nose with her handkerchief. Afterwards she was glad, for the gesture served another purpose. It kept her from crying out.

The balloon shot up into the sky.

Then Leontine did cry out. A panic seized her that her husband would disappear into the clouds, never to return. She raised her arms as if to draw him back to earth.

Floating far above her, Thad saw Leontine's upstretched arms and thought she was waving. He leaned over the edge of the basket, grinning. Then he picked up a small megaphone and called:

"This is great!"

His voice calmed her. Suddenly she realized the balloon was only a few hundred feet over her head and securely tethered to the ground. This was, after all, Thad's first ascent. Free ballooning was for the experts.

"But you might as well get used to it," Leontine reminded herself severely. "After all, he's not yet twenty-five. This is indeed only the beginning!"

During the next year the baby Louisa gave Leontine very little time to watch her husband's ascensions. Thad decided almost immediately that his first balloon was too small to investigate the upper air currents or conduct meteorological studies. He began to take passengers aloft for the sizable sum of $1.00 apiece. Thus he might earn money for a larger balloon. Meanwhile he practiced free ballooning, finally becoming adept enough to offer his more daring customers a real sky ride for $5.00, a handsome price.

Thad's letters to his father about his work so intrigued Clovis Lowe that he decided to visit his son. Meeting Leontine and his granddaughter, Louisa, was a pleasant excuse. Actually he spent every day with Thad, watching and learning all he could about ballooning. As the weeks stretched into months, Clovis became an accomplished aeronaut himself.

The larger balloon was begun in the spring of 1858. It was well toward completion when Thad was asked to go to Ottawa, Canada, with a circus to celebrate the laying of the Atlantic cable.

The new balloon was rushed to completion for the event. Almost twice as large as the first, it was made of the finest India silk, heavily starched with a rice mixture. The netting, too, was of silk twine, much lighter yet stronger than the cheaper cotton twine used on the first balloon.

"We'll call it the *Enterprise,*" Leontine decided, "because it has been an undertaking to build and it promises bold ventures to come."

The first Atlantic cable, completed in September, 1858, occasioned fairs and fireworks throughout the British Isles, Canada, and the United States. Hailed as the "Nuptials of Old Europe with Young America," the impact on civilization of "the lightning under the ocean" was likened to the introduction of steam on the Erie Canal. Queen Victoria sent the first transatlantic wire message, while the *Te Deum* was sung at Trinity Church in New York.

Hucksters even sold all-day suckers made in the form of twisted cables.

It was an unbelievable letdown when the marvelous invention only ten days later developed "temporary difficulties": crackled and sputtered ineffectually, and was forever stilled.

But Thad's exhibitions at Ottawa were a personal success. Besides the publicity afforded by this first public appearance, he was honored to meet Professor Samuel Morse, inventor of the cable, and Cyrus W. Field, whose financial support had made the transatlantic wire possible.

Immediately on his return to New York, he started work on another airship which he planned to equip with every instrument available for study of the upper air. Certain of the existence of constant air currents, he wished to discover if the rivers of the sky might not be conductors of weather as well as aircraft.

His early findings satisfied him that his supposition was basically correct. He began to send his data to the Smithsonian Institute at Washington, having in mind a national bureau with a system of weather warnings to aid the farmer, mariner—and aeronaut.

Meanwhile he worked constantly to improve on the design and operation of aerostats. One such aid was an instrument to measure latitude and longitude from the air. Thaddeus called it an "altimeter," though the barometer was actually used to ascertain height.

He perfected a new varnish to coat the gas bag which prevented rapid dissipation of the gas, a major problem when attempting long distance flights. Thad's concoction made his balloon buoyant for two weeks or more.

His painstaking craftsmanship brought orders for Lowe aircraft from all over the country. He bought a piece of Mr. Stevens' farm in Hoboken, where he erected a large shed. There dozens of workmen, personally trained by Thaddeus, turned out balloons to be shipped as far away as California.

The birth of his second daughter, Ida Alpha, spurred Thad to purchase a town house and employ a cook and maid as well as a nurse for the babies. The Lowe's drawing room became a meeting place for scientists, journalists, businessmen, outstanding people from every field, attracted not only by Thad's work, but by the couple's natural poise and intelligence.

Conversation invariably turned to the possibilities of air travel. The slowness of communications between America and the Continent was a constant irritation.

"There's little hope of a new cable in the foreseeable future," one gentleman complained, as he sipped brandy one May evening in 1859. "Most promising for a speedier link with England is this new ship, the *Great Eastern.* They say she will cross the ocean in a week or less. But my word, even at that rate, the market could change a dozen times while one is waiting for news!"

"I believe a transoceanic airship is one answer," Thaddeus remarked quietly. "Buoyancy is limited only by size. Make the gas envelope large enough and passengers, freight, even troops could be carried. Such an airship could cross the ocean in three or four days."

His friends looked at him in amazement.

"No ship has ever stayed aloft for so long a period!"

"How could it be propelled and navigated?"

"Perhaps Professor Lowe is thinking of a larger version of Henri Giffard's steam-powered dirigible airship," offered one newsman. "He made a successful trip across France back in 1852."

"No engine has yet been invented powerful enough to push so large an aircraft against the lightest breeze," Thad asserted. "The currents of the air would have to be ridden as a sailing vessel rides the wind. Properly used, the currents aloft are steady, and strong enough to waft a balloon across the sea at an undreamed of speed."

The idea was immediately seized upon by the press. Columnists and cartoonists had an imaginative field day, caricaturing the projected airship with acid pens.

Thad's rivals were vehement. John Wise, "King of the Aeronauts," denounced Thad as a publicity seeking showman, no scientist at all. Such sharp criticism from a man he had admired and hoped to work with was a bitter pill for Thad, especially since he knew Wise's motives were selfish.

For Wise himself had already begun construction of an airship for the ocean flight. Wise's *Atlantic* was to be the largest balloon yet built, with a spherical bag 60 feet in diameter, having a capacity for 50,000 cubic feet of gas.

At least Thad had the satisfaction of knowing Wise considered him a serious challenge to his own leadership in aeronautics, for now the elder balloonist rushed his mammoth aerostat to completion. The trial flight from St. Louis to New York was announced for early July, 1859. Another of Thad's rivals, John La Mountain, a man only two years his senior, was chosen to assist Wise. Mr. Hyde of the *St. Louis Republican* and O. A. Gager, millionaire balloon enthusiast who was backing the trip, were to be passengers.

On the Fourth of July, Thad was en route to Maine, to give an exhibition, so he did not immediately hear the results of Wise's flight. An old friend, Neal Dow, the mayor of Portland, told him the details.

"Wise made a distance record all right," Dow told him—"travelled 800 miles in 19 hours and landed up in Jefferson County, New York. But what a ride they had!" Dow chuckled reminiscently. "They were almost blown into Lake Erie in a storm. The waves were too high to use the boat so they cut her loose to gain altitude. Then they went skimming over the treetops. Just pure luck they landed in one piece. But I guess that's all ballooning is, luck."

"It shouldn't be luck if you can forecast the weather and know your currents."

"Maybe so, maybe so." Dow shrugged and started to chuckle again. "One paper reported that an old lady ran out into the field where they landed. She'd watched them come in and wanted to get a closer look at the aeronauts. After sizing them up, she allowed she'd never thought to see such sensible looking gentlemen in so outlandish a vehicle!"

Thad's July 4th exhibition in Portland consisted of going aloft and releasing 33 small balloons, one for each state in the Union. Ships docking during the next week reported sighting the gaily colored toys as much as 600 miles at sea. That was all the proof Thad needed. If little balloons, treated with his special varnish, could remain aloft so long and fly so far, the aerostat he had in mind could surely cross the sea.

On July 15th, Thad notified the newspapers that he had started construction of a giant airship for the transatlantic flight. The gas bag would measure 130 feet from valve to neck, having a transverse diameter of 104 feet. Its gas capacity of 725,000 cubic feet was over five times that of Wise's *Atlantic*. It was to be named the *City of New York*.

"And if he ever gets it inflated," one reporter exclaimed, "it'll be the biggest thing in the city of New York!"

CHAPTER FIVE

THE *CITY OF NEW YORK*

All Thad's years of work and study were incorporated into the *City of New York.* He was determined it should be not only the largest, but the most perfect areostat in history.

Throughout the summer, Thad sweated beside his workmen in the construction shed on the flats of Hoboken, superintending every phase of the building.

The buzzing of seventeen Wheeler and Wilson sewing machines enhanced the workroom's resemblance to an outsize beehive. Six thousand yards of the finest twilled cloth, cut in narrow panels, were being stitched together with triple seams to make the gas envelope. One hundred women sewing for two years could not have finished the job.

Close by, a dozen men painstakingly wove a network of flaxen cord to encase the envelope. Miles of the fine material must be worked into an intricate pattern. Stronger even than the silk used on the *Enterprise,* Thad calculated the casing must withstand strain up to 160 tons.

The car in which the scientists and crew would ride demanded skillful planning. The open basket in which aeronauts were exposed to the elements and the nauseous smell of coal gas would not do for so long a trip. It must be completely enclosed and heated.

Thad designed the round compartment as large as possible, a comfortable twenty feet in circumference, the size of an average drawing room. Still, with the men and equipment to be carried, every inch must be planned for maximum use.

The rattan basket was chest high, enclosed with canvas which was stretched upwards to form the roof. A seat girdled the interior, above which windows were cut in the canvas. Between and around the windows were pegs and ridges for the instruments, while beneath the seat were coffers for provisions.

A small lime stove would be used to heat the chamber. The flameless heater was the invention and contribution of Mr. O. A. Gager, the wealthy balloonist who had helped John Wise build his *Atlantic.* It was designed especially for use in aerostats, where a coal or wood stove would be too dangerous so close to highly flammable gasses.

After the long hot days, Thaddeus sat up nights planning for the trip and inventing new aids to navigation and "philosophical apparatus" for meteorological observation. In between, he somehow found time to give lectures describing the airship and explaining his aims. The public must be made aware that this was no stunt.

He assured his audiences, "This project is a serious endeavor to further aeronautics. I am neither rash, insane, nor a seeker after fame, though cartoonists and certain of my rivals would have it thought so. I have given the matter of the Atlantic voyage cool consideration.

"In the past few years, tremendous progress has been made in the construction and management of balloons. We have increased knowledge of the upper air currents whose existence was established by such pioneers as Charles Green and John Wise.

"It is a tribute to the safety of ballooning that of 3000

aeronauts to emerge during the past fifty years, only one-eighth of that number could be called truly competent. Yet statistics show air travel to be less hazardous than any other mode of transportation. In that time 8000 persons made aerial voyages with only one life lost—and that through carelessness.

"That no more rapid progress in aeronautics has been made is due largely to the fact that seven-eighths of our balloonists are not practical investigators but exhibitors, making limited ascensions for money.

"I would be the last to deny that exhibition ascensions have their place. It is through them I have financed my scientific projects to date, including this last and greatest one.

"But," and here Thad paused to be sure he had full attention, "if there is nothing but talk and theory, the aeronautic art will never progress beyond its present state. I say it is time someone made a bold push!"

Using colored diagrams to illustrate his points, Thaddeus explained the theory behind so large an aerostat.

"Buoyancy is largely contingent on the amount of gas contained in the bag. Fully inflated, the *City of New York* will have a lifting power of 22½ tons if hydrogen is used, 11½ tons if filled with coal gas." Anyone could understand that those figures added up to a lot of passengers and freight.

". . . and with the fabric sealed by my special varnish, loss of gas will be reduced to a minimum. My ship will be able to remain aloft much longer than the estimated three days it should take to cross the Atlantic."

Thad described with pride the mechanical appliances and navigational aids he had invented. Foremost among these was the long dreamed of propeller wheel which would raise and lower the ship without valving precious gas or tossing ballast.

Even the sceptics had to admit Thad's ideas were basically sound—if they worked.

"If they work," people were saying to each other, "the air can be traversed as easily as land or sea!" Then they shook their heads. The thought was too revolutionary to comprehend.

Visitors flocked to the construction shed to see the huge balloon for themselves. The crowds hampered the work, but Thad was publicity wise enough to realize they must not be discouraged.

One afternoon in mid-August he was sweating over a cauldron of his varnish when a writer from the *Scientific American* approached him.

After introducing himself, the writer leaned curiously over the bubbling liquid then drew back quickly, making a wry face.

"What in thunder is that villainous smelling stuff?" he asked.

"That," replied Thad, "is my special varnish. It is boiling at a temperature of 600°, which is the only fact about it I intend to reveal even to your distinguished periodical."

Thad wiped his face with a clean white handkerchief. "If you don't think that's hot work under an August sun, just join me and see."

"I'll take your word for that, Professor," his visitor laughed. "I was hoping to interrupt you long enough for a conducted tour. We'd like to tell our readers something about your inventions, but I confess, I must have you explain them to me."

Thad knew that an article published in the *Scientific American* would establish him once and for all as a serious scientist. Calling one of his workmen to watch and stir the varnish, he rolled down his sleeves and shrugged into his working jacket.

"A reporter and an artist from *Harper's Weekly* were here only last week," he remarked as they strolled toward the construction shed. "They seemed particularly interested in the Francis metallic lifeboat. I'll show you that first."

The boat was 30 feet long with a seven-foot beam. It carried a mutton-shoulder sail and the hull was divided into watertight compartments.

"It is as unsinkable as a boat can be," Thad pointed out, "because even if one part of the hull is injured, water can get into only the damaged section. Several compartments would have to flood before she would sink. I've named her *Leontine* in honor of my wife."

"Why, your lifeboat is as large as many vessels that have crossed the Atlantic," exclaimed his companion.

"I still prefer to go all the way by air," Thaddeus assured him.

"Is the little Ericsson caloric engine intended for use as an auxiliary to the sail?"

"No, no," replied Thad, "that is to work the propeller wheel which you see here in the stern of the *Leontine*. The engine is only four horsepower, too small to drive so large a boat. But when the fan wheel is pitched just so it will drive the balloon either up or down to seek the proper current, or it can keep the aircraft from spinning in a high wind."

"What you might call a steadying influence," laughed the reporter.

"Exactly. It will enable us to keep steerageway under

circumstances that formerly would have put the balloon out of control.

"The lifeboat will be covered with India rubber so extra provisions may be stowed in it. I intend to carry food and wine for six months in case we are driven off course and must land in the African desert or some other uninhabited spot. Since it will be kept dry by the covering, rockets and roman candles will be safely stored here also. The boat will be connected to the passenger basket by a rope ladder."

Thad reached down and picked up a large rubber object from the bottom of the boat. His interviewer exclaimed as Thad spread it on the ground:

"Why it looks like a man!"

"As it should, for I constructed it to cover a man. The India-rubber suit can be inflated to support its occupant in the water for an indefinite period while also protecting him against the cold."

The gentleman from the *Scientific American* was now completely enthralled.

"To go back for a moment, Professor," he was saying, "to the function of the propeller wheel. You say it will drive the aerostat up and down to seek the proper current. How will you know at what level that current prevails?"

"I have a simple device for that purpose. A cord about a mile and a-half long with a lead weight on the end will be suspended from the aerostat at all times. Different colored flags will be attached at intervals, each color denoting a certain level. If we find ourselves in an adverse current, we discover through the telescope which flag is being blown in the proper direction—in this case always to the east—then start the fanwheel and push the balloon down to that stream."

"But if you must go up it would be guesswork?"

"On take-off, I shall ascend at once to a height of three or four miles where the easterly current nearly always prevails."

"A rarefied atmosphere to remain in long, Professor."

"Nor will we, sir. I like to keep within a respectable distance of mundane things where I can see folks and communicate with them. For this reason we will carry, besides the usual speaking trumpets and horns, 100 India-rubber bags attached to small silk parachutes. In these, copies of the ship's log will be dropped on towns and surface vessels over which we pass."

"If thorough preparation could insure success, you certainly deserve it, Professor."

"I shall deliver the Monday *New York Times* in London on Wednesday or go in the ocean," Thad quipped. Then he added seriously, "My backers have already invested $20,000 in this project. I shall do everything in my power to deserve their confidence."

In October the *City of New York* was moved to the Crystal Palace grounds at Reservoir Square to be prepared for the trial flight, scheduled for November 1st. As the day approached, merchants in the area displayed bunting and flags to welcome the crowds that arrived by trolley, stage, carriage, on foot or horseback, to view the wonderful airship that would fly across the sea.

The attention of the world had been focused on Reservoir Square by excited newsmen in America, England, and Europe. *Harper's Weekly* proclaimed the *City of New York* "an engineering triumph in any age," while the *Scientific American* praised Thad's effort with unaccustomed enthusiasm.

"The dimensions of the *City of New York* so far exceed those of any balloon previously constructed that the bare fact of its existence is notable," the magazine declared. "Whether successful or not, it merits mention for the magnitude, energy, and fertility of resource displayed in its prosecution. The introduction of valuable improvements leads to the conviction that the general arrangement is greatly superior."

Thad checked and rechecked with the gas company to be certain they could produce the necessary 500,000 cubic feet of gas within 24 hours.

"During inflation," he explained to the company representative, "a certain amount of gas escapes. The longer it takes to fill the bag, the more gas dissipates. Unless the mains can produce sufficient gas in the 24-hour period to inflate the balloon, so much will escape that the ship will never get off the ground."

The man patiently assured Thad that he understood and inflation was begun on schedule the afternoon before the trial.

When Thad arrived home that evening he was set upon by two small cyclones that were his daughters.

"Tomorrow Mama is going to take us to see you go up in the sky in the big balloon!" cried three-year-old Louisa. "Ida can go too, but not Leon. He's too little." Leon was their new baby brother.

"Someday, little one," replied her father tiredly, "but not tomorrow."

"*Tiens*! Then what has gone wrong?" asked Leontine. She followed Thad down the hall to his study where she found him sitting in his leather chair, head in hands.

"A dozen times I told them—I must have 500,000 cubic feet in 24 hours." Thad shrugged. "They thought I said 50,000 cubic feet! Now, with people already gathering to see the trial, the press all over the world alerted—now they tell me that their largest pipe cannot deliver 50,000 cubic feet within 24 hours! It does not require much calculation to see that, at that rate, there would be a continuous inflation and no ascension!"

"Well, certainly people will know the trial is postponed because of the gas company's error and through no fault of yours," his wife reasoned.

"Oh yes. The reporters will see to that. But I shall have to put off my trip till next year in any case. By the time I make other arrangements winter will be upon us."

Thousands of citizens in and around New York who had been watching for the seagoing balloon, took out their disappointment in letters to their editors. The gas company which Thad gladly turned over to the public as a sacrifice was roundly trounced. In the end, the whole sad sequence of events had, for the Lowes, a happy ending.

Within the week, Thad received a letter from Professor John C. Cresson, President of the Benjamin Franklin Institute of Sciences at Philadelphia. As spokesman for a group of prominent businessmen and scientists, he begged Thad to bring his airship to their city, all transportation costs to be paid by them. The Philadelphians avowedly derived a "fierce joy" from this opportunity to show up New York.

"And there will be no question of not getting sufficient gas," Thad told Leontine after reading the letter, "because, my dear, Professor Cresson is also Chairman of the Board of the Point Breeze Gas Works of Philadelphia!"

Thad took his family to Charleston, South Carolina for the winter while the *City of New York* was stored in Hoboken. In April, Thad returned briefly to New York to supervise the loading of the airship onto two freight cars for transportation to its new home.

Professor Cresson had already prepared a mooring spot near the Point Breeze Gas Works and was as anxious as Thad to speed preparations for the Atlantic voyage. The committee backing the flight had some misgivings, however.

Letters and treatises had been pouring into the newspapers all winter from so-called professors and "atmospheric voyagers." Some of these stated positively that such a huge aerostat could never be gotten off the ground, or if it rose at all, it would be unmanageable because of its bulk.

Nevertheless the trial flight was scheduled for June 28th. In the meantime Thad made several exhibition ascensions. One was in honor of a Japanese Embassy, members of which Asiatic nation had never before visited American soil. The prince and his noblemen, resplendent, if uncomfortably warm, in heavy brocade robes, declared they would never forget the vision of American ships that "sail in the air."

The *City of New York* was renamed the *Great Western,* at the suggestion of a New York newspaperman, Horace Greeley. The name was apt since the *Great Eastern,* the world's largest seagoing vessel, was also to make her maiden voyage that spring.

During final preparations for the trial, a stranger who appeared to be a sea captain began to frequent the field. He watched with interest the activity around the airship and asked endless questions, until the ground crew complained to Thad that he was interfering with their work. Thad collared the man and asked him what his business might be.

"Captain John B. Dickinson, at your service, sir. That

your contraption?" he waved at the balloon, and when Thad replied in the affirmative, he said, "I've sailed the seven seas and never seen the like. You mean to cross the Atlantic Ocean in her, I read by the papers."

"That is correct, Captain," Thad said politely. "And I must say, even if you have sailed the seven seas, you still haven't lived till you've flown."

"Now that's just what I figure, young man. You'll be needin' someone to sail that pert little boat," the seaman indicated the *Leontine,* "in case your airship founders. So I just thought I'd come along over and see if you needed a hand."

Thad had his first recruit for the Atlantic voyage.

CHAPTER SIX

THE *GREAT WESTERN* AFLOAT

Thad and Captain Dickinson drove out to Point Breeze at dawn on the momentous Thursday, June 28th, 1860. They were accompanied by the editor of the *Philadelphia Inquirer,* Mr. Garrick Mallery, who was to be passenger of honor on the trial flight.

Professor Cresson was already on the field, superintending the inflation of the *Great Western*'s giant gas envelope, when the three men arrived. He had installed special 20-inch mains with meters to check the gas as it flowed through.

"Well, Thad," Professor Cresson greeted him, "she's going great! You'll have 400,000 cubic feet of gas in the envelope in four hours."

Thad checked the meter and nodded satisfaction. Then he looked up at the sky. "It's a clear, still morning, John. We'll have no trouble today. But we must get a high fence installed to protect the balloon during inflation. If a wind comes up before she's ready, we'll be in trouble."

Garrick Mallery stood back a little, watching the proceedings. As the morning progressed he found himself jostled by a curious crowd. Some loudly ridiculed the whole procedure and threatened the aeronauts with every conceivable mishap. Many recognizing the newsman, began to cajole and even bribe him tearfully not to risk his life in an untried experiment.

Mallery later wrote scornfully that these were all a part of "the large and respectable class who never believe aught but their senses.

"We, on the contrary, were so unscientific as to feel much more secure in the magnitude of our conveyance, particularly after a careful inspection of its great strength and *manifold skillful appliances.* Besides, it was contrary to nature that the *Philadelphia Inquirer* should not be well up in everything."

With relief Mallery saw the balloon begin to tug at the mooring ropes. Just after noon, Thad signalled to him and Dickinson to climb into the car. Some mooring ropes were already loosed. Strong arms held the cables as the ship was tried for lift. Fortunately no air stirred, for even with all sandbags attached the upward tug was terrific.

Thaddeus began to toss out ballast as the ropes were let go one by one. The balloon was already swaying back and forth, striving for its natural element, when there was a loud "halloo" from below. The three men in the car stared as two young men leapt aboard.

"Made our last dying speech and confession," one of them said breathlessly, by way of explanation.

Thaddeus shrugged and turned to the business at hand. Mallery saw him throw out one or two more bags of ballast, then break the neck of the gas envelope to let it "blow off." The stench was momentarily overpowering so when next the editor looked, he perceived with amazement the fields receding lower and lower.

"Why, we're off!" cried Mallery, though he hardly believed it. There was no feeling of motion. The people below were cheering, waving, even running futilely after them. Mallery picked up two flags and waved them out the window as he saw the other passengers do.

When the balloon stabilized at a few hundred feet, Thad climbed up in the hoop, a device between car and gas bag to which were toggled all the guide ropes. Ordinarily flyers took turns up there throughout the voyage. Since Thad was the only qualified aeronaut on this short trip, he would have to go back and forth between there and the car.

Having checked his lines, Thaddeus remained aloft to enjoy for a few minutes alone the culmination of two years' labor, and many more of planning and study. Every conceivable obstacle had been thrown in his way, so that he himself had moments of self-doubt, surrounded as he was by unbelievers. But his "unmanageable bulk" had taken to the air with the ease and grace of a swallow.

He let out a whoop that caused his passengers to look up alarmed. "Here at last is the *Great Western* afloat, after all the prophecies against her!" he cried triumphantly. The men smiled and waved.

Thaddeus remained low over the city to give spectators below a good view of this ship that "could not be got off the ground." His passengers were ecstatic at their first view of the world from the air. Mallery felt that only the balloon car had reality as he looked down on a toy city with miniature parks, buildings and radiating streets.

Directly over the *Inquirer* office Thad shouted to toss more ballast and they shot upwards again. Stabilizing at one mile, the balloon began to travel a more easterly course. Over the Delaware River, Mallery pointed out that the bottom could be seen with the naked eye. Through the large telescope he swore he could make out stones in its bed.

Late in the afternoon the *Great Western* sailed majestically over Camden, New Jersey, and followed the Camden & Atlantic Railroad across fertile fields towards the sea.

Thaddeus had shown his passengers how the instruments operated. Mallery noted on the barometer that they were now at a height of three miles, moving eastward at about 60 miles per hour. The sea was clearly visible through the glass, and the earth appeared convex instead of concave.

The rarefied air gave everyone a sense of exhiliration. One by one they climbed the ladder onto the hoop and sang lustily. The echo from the balloon gave their voices a stentorian quality.

Here above the clouds the sky was very blue and the moon shone as bright as at midnight. Thad pointed out that for the poor earthlings the sun had nearly set, but up here it lit the clouds with unearthly tints his passengers had never before seen.

As the sun disappeared the gas contracted causing a rather rapid descent. Thad decided to land rather than toss ballast or set the propeller wheel in motion.

They were low over a town which later proved to be Medford, and close enough to see a crowd of upturned faces in some sand flats nearby. The people were gesticulating and shouting, obviously inviting the flyers to land.

It was growing dark rapidly, so Thad called through his trumpet to the men below to catch the trailing rope he was about to let go. Then, instructing his passengers to bend their knees and hold tightly to the car's edge, he allowed the gas to escape freely.

The posture assumed by the flyers was standard for landing procedure, but so expert was Thaddeus' handling it proved an unnecessary precaution. He seldom used the grapnel except in a high wind, since it made for a bumpy landing. Tonight he set his giant down so softly on a sand dune that his passengers hardly realized the moment when they touched earth.

Garrick Mallery wrote later: "The monster in ascent and descent and in that generally most difficult matter of landing, was as thoroughly under the control of its skillful builder as ever a horse in harness."

He further declared himself thoroughly convinced of the possibility of an Atlantic flight. "We could easily . . . have been over the sea at short notice, in a steady current of 100 miles per hour. It is a curious coincidence that, on this 28th day of June, 1860, the *Great Eastern,* largest seagoing vessel, arrived, inaugurating, it is said, a new system of ocean navigation, and on the same day, the *Great Western,* still larger in proportion to rivals of its own kind, left the city of Philadelphia to commence a yet more novel era in the navigation of the air."

By the first week in September final preparations for the ocean flight were complete. The coffers were tightly provisioned and an adequate crew was assembled. During the summer a number of foresighted citizens had added their names to the list of subscribers backing the Atlantic voyage. One letter containing an offer of assistance was particularly gratifying to Thad.

He brought it to Leontine one evening as she sat sewing in the garden. "Look at that," he cried triumphantly.

Leontine read it aloud: "I have read with great interest the success of your recent trial flight. On your trip across the Atlantic you would be immensely benefited by my years of experience. I should be happy to join forces with you, freely lending my distinguished name to your enterprise."

It was signed "John Wise."

"But he's been your severest critic!" exclaimed Leontine.

"Indeed. I'd say he's led the barrage of jeers. No one has more earnestly tried to discredit my every effort."

"Then what will you do about this?" Leontine waved the letter.

"Just this," replied Thad. Taking the paper from her he set it afire. As it flamed up, he held it aloft like a torch until he had to drop it. Then he carefully stamped every remnant to cinders.

Thad's most treasured praise came from the head of the Smithsonian Institution at Washington. Professor Joseph Henry wrote:

"The Smithsonian Institution has long been aware of the work and theories of Professor Lowe and we have found his statements scientifically sound. It is with a great pleasure and satisfaction that we welcome proof of his genius. We shall follow the outcome of his plan with interest."

On the morning of Friday, September 7th, crowds gathered at Point Breeze to watch the inflation. About eleven o'clock a strong wind sprang up and Thad instructed the men to stop the flow of gas until it died down.

The yellowish red canvas of the partially filled balloon looked like an overgrown half-ripened tomato. The neck, stretched limply across the ground, resembled a bologna sausage. People pressed in on every side to get a better view of the curious contrivance.

It was four o'clock before inflation could be resumed. Most of the crowd had dispersed leaving only a few enthusiasts. The *Inquirer*'s special aerial edition was on hand since Thad still planned to take off the moment inflation was complete. Garrick Mallery felt the American papers would cause quite a stir in London literary circles.

The balloon was nearly full when the Rev. Dr. Newton

of St. Paul's Episcopal Church presented the voyagers with a Bible and addressed a few words to those assembled.

"The Creator has given man dominion over the birds of the air and the beasts of the earth and the fishes of the sea," proclaimed Dr. Newton. He declared his belief that man was meant to navigate the air as well as land or sea, and that the time would come when man would indeed have as practical dominion in this last area as in the other two.

He commended the explorers to Almighty God, begging Him to look graciously on their undertaking. "Guard Thy servants, we beseech Thee, from all the dangers of the atmosphere, from adverse winds, from storm and tempest . . ."

At 5:30 the wind sprang up again. Thad decided it would be too great a risk to continue inflation in such a gale. The grounds were cleared, and the flight again postponed, though this time only until the next day.

Towards noon on Saturday, the *Great Western* began to tug at her moorings. The car was attached. All was in readiness.

"This is it!" cried Thad to his crew. "Let us waste no time getting off!"

He dashed towards the edge of the enclosure where Leontine stood.

"Goodbye, my darling, oh, do be careful. Good luck, good luck!" Leontine reached up to kiss him. Suddenly there was a rending sound behind them.

A gust of wind had caught the balloon and torn a 50 foot gap in the fabric. Within an instant the airship careened to one side, and with a dreadful hiss, collapsed. Thad stood for the moment, rooted, as Leontine grasped his arm in anguish.

"I begged them," he whispered, "I begged them to erect

a wooden guard to protect her during inflation. I was a fool not to insist!"

The grounds were a scene of the wildest confusion and excitement. Someone said that one of the workmen had been caught beneath the falling canvas. The rumor was squelched only when the fellow appeared quite unharmed.

Captain Dickinson wept unashamedly as he saw his hopes literally dashed to the ground. Only when Professor Cresson and Thaddeus assured him it was just a temporary annoyance did he pull himself together.

Thad remained calm and philosophical. "This has proved one thing. My balloon can endure any strain it might ordinarily be subjected to." Several onlookers, including the observant reporter, Garrick Mallery, attested that the strain had reduced the anchor cables to half their normal diameter. "Doubtless we'll be off in a couple of weeks," Thad continued with more conviction than he felt.

The *Great Western* and Thad did try again on September 29th. He anxiously watched the final moments of inflation, beads of perspiration standing out on his forehead, though the weather had already turned cool. Suddenly he cried:

"Hold! For the love of Heaven, hold!"

An ominous bulge had appeared at the point of repair. In that moment Thad knew this year would not see the culmination of his dream. The *Great Western* was in for a major overhaul.

CHAPTER SEVEN

FLY EAST, YOUNG MAN—

With a heavy heart Thad once again supervised the winter storing of the *Great Western.*

"Cheer up, Thaddeus," Professor Cresson advised, "you're bound to make it next year. We'll have to replace several gores on that side of the bag, but she'll be as good as new then, maybe better."

"I've exhausted my funds, John, and Leontine is expecting again. I guess I'll have to pack my fleet and travel around doing exhibitions, pick up more orders for sporting balloons."

"Your committee is still behind you all the way, you know that, don't you, Thad?" Cresson assured him.

"I appreciate their faith, John," Thad answered. "But what's left of the flight fund must be kept intact. I am anxious to continue with my weather experiments. I should have been able to forecast the strength of the wind that ripped the balloon. Traveling around the country will enable me to gather valuable data from various points above this continent."

Thad returned home that evening to find Leontine red-eyed, the children strangely quiet.

"My father has been murdered on the streets of Paris by royalist brigands!" Leontine's voice was dull with shock and incredulity.

Pere Gaschon had gone back during the summer to his

rebellion-torn homeland, where royalists and republicans alike plotted the overthrow of Napoleon III's uneasy throne. The old soldier had felt he could somehow further the cause of the Republic.

"He was shot down in the street like a common criminal, and left to die in the gutter!" Leontine cried angrily.

"He died a soldier, dearest," Thad assured her, "fighting in his own way for democracy and freedom against tyranny."

Leontine shook her head sadly. "I pray that this country may never be torn apart by civil war—brother against brother, father against son. One cannot realize how horrible it is until . . ." She leaned against Thad a moment, speechless with grief for her father and her country. Then with sudden realization, she exclaimed, "Poor Maman! Should I not go to her immediately in New York?"

"You must not travel now," Thad admonished. "Why don't you write her this evening and ask her to visit you here? She hasn't seen you or the children since we left New York."

The next evening after dinner, Professor Cresson and several members of the flight committee called to express their sympathy.

"Shocking!" exclaimed one gentleman. "The unsettled conditions in Europe have gone on too long. Even the United States is infected with unrest. This slave question is a knotty one. The Abolitionists condemn the system as immoral and unchristian, and rightly so. Yet the whole economy of the South is built on slave labor. Friends in the Capital tell me that friction between North and South has reached a danger point."

Leontine looked frightened. "Surely they would not

fight! One heard talk in Charleston last winter, but I did not believe the situation would come to an open rift!"

"Gentlemen," Thad interrupted, not wanting his wife upset again, "I have brandy and cigars awaiting you in the library."

As the men passed down the hall from the reception room, Thad put his arm around Leontine. "Don't let their talk fret you, my dear," he said. "Problems are solved by peaceful, legal means in these United States. The southerners themselves will see that slavery has no place in a country dedicated to freedom and equality. Now run upstairs and rest."

The children tucked away, Leontine had slipped into her negligee and was settled on her chaise longue to read, when her husband burst into the bedroom. She could sense his excitement, though he handed her the letter he held in his hand without a word. Leontine looked up questioningly as she began to read:

> To Professor Joseph Henry, Secretary of the Smithsonian Institution, Washington, D.C.
>
> The undersigned citizens of Philadelphia have taken a deep interest in the attempt of Mr. T. S. C. Lowe to cross the Atlantic by aeronautic machinery, and have confidence that his extensive preparations to effect that object will greatly add to scientific knowledge.

". . . as indeed they already have," interjected Leontine, then went back to the letter.

> Mr. Lowe has individually spent much time and money in the enterprise, and in addition the citizens of Philadelphia have contributed several thousand dollars to further his efforts in demonstrating the feasibility of transatlantic air navigation. With reliance upon Mr. Lowe and his plans we cheerfully recommend him to the favorable

> consideration of the Smithsonian Institution, and trust such aid and advice will be furnished him by that distinguished body as may assist in the success of the attempt, in which we take a deep interest.

Leontine read the signatures over slowly: "John C. Cresson; William Hamilton; W. H. Harrison; Fairman Rogers; John C. Fisher; Thomas Stewardson, M.D.; J. B. Lippincott; George W. Childs; John Grigg; S. S. Haldeman; John E. Frazer; George Harding; Morton McMichael."

"Why I don't believe so distinguished a group of names have met together on one document since the signing of the Declaration of Independence!" she cried excitedly. "You will go at once to Washington, of course, and consult with the great Professor Henry."

"Well, sometime this winter. No hurry," replied Thad.

"What is this 'no hurry,' " said Leontine, taking Thad by the shoulders. "You are the one to put thought into action *zut!, comme ca,*" and she snapped her dainty fingers. "Surely you do not hesitate because of me?"

"We'll talk about it tomorrow." Thad kissed her, rose, and made hastily for the door. "The men are still here."

The next day the postman brought a letter from Mere Gaschon. There could be no better balm for her wound, the poor woman asserted, than to spend a few weeks with her darling daughter and grandchildren, and perhaps attend the advent of the fourth!

"So," Leontine was triumphant. "See how nicely everything works out."

Professor Henry was a red-headed Scotchman, equal in height and breadth to Thad. His blue eyes twinkled as he grasped the balloonist's hand and drew him into the office.

"So you're going to fly the Atlantic," Henry went right to the point.

Thaddeus studied the scientist's broad face to detect any signs of sarcasm. He was accustomed to scepticism, even derision, from people when first confronted with the idea. It was difficult to realize that here was one man who needed no convincing.

"It has been fully established," Henry continued, waving Thad to a seat near his desk, "by continuous observation collected at this institution over a period of ten years from every part of the United States that, as a general rule, all the meteorological phenomena advance from west to east, and that the higher clouds always move eastwardly."

The big man paced his office speaking with deliberation. "I do not hesitate therefore to say that, provided a balloon is of sufficient size and sufficiently impermeable to gas—that is, if it can stay aloft a sufficient length of time, it would indeed be wafted across the Atlantic."

Henry held up his hand as Thad started to speak.

"Your *Great Western* fills the qualifications. Your aeronautics are unassailably sound. But I'd like to see you try a long flight overland before tackling the ocean."

Thad shrugged. "I couldn't attempt the ocean flight until spring. Might as well keep in practice."

"Good boy! I'll write my friend Murat Halstead, editor of the *Cincinnati Commercial*. He's interested in ballooning and would arrange all the details. Cincinnati's as good a starting point as any."

Throughout the winter of 1860-1861 the two scientists worked together collecting meteorological data for the United States Weather Bureau they hoped to establish. During the same winter six southern states, led by South Carolina, seceded from the Union.

Thad saw no reason to change his flight plans. The government would reprimand its disobedient citizens and bring them back into the fold. In March, he left Washington for Cincinnati to start the overland flight he hoped would be the first leg of his transatlantic journey.

Professor Henry had a word of advice before he left.

"I have had some interesting experiences with the public," he told Thad, "and it is very difficult to get them to take new devices seriously; almost every new scientific theory is laughed at.

"Now we know that, on any given day, whatever may be the direction of the wind at the surface of the earth, a balloon elevated sufficiently high would be carried easterly by the prevailing current in the upper, or rather middle region of the atmosphere.

"If you wish to make a really good impression on the public, start with everything apparently against you—in a word, on a day when the surface winds are westerly. Otherwise they're bound to say you waited till conditions were just right—or even that you were plain lucky."

Thad traveled first to Philadelphia for a brief visit with his family, which now included a third daughter, Ava Eugenie, and to get the *Enterprise* out of storage. The *Enterprise* was still his favorite balloon. Only slightly smaller than Wise's *Atlantic,* it was a steady ship, reliable and easy to handle.

Thad arrived in Cincinnati to find its citizens already excited about his forthcoming flight. Murat Halstead was responsible for the advance publicity as well as for arranging lectures for Thad.

The next two weeks were a bustle of preparations, mixed with speeches given at banquets and luncheons, finally culminating in a huge public address at the Opera House.

Everything was ready but the weather. Snow and rain fell persistently.

The *Commercial* reported the firing on Fort Sumter on April 12th, 1861 and the surrender of Major Robert Anderson and his garrison on the 14th. There was a great deal of discussion about the rebellion in the south and further threats of secession. Still, in Cincinnati, as elsewhere throughout the North, it was conceded that nothing would come of it all but a few skirmishes and verbal brickbats.

Thaddeus, for one, was too busy to give the matter much thought. On April 19th, two days after Virginia seceded, Halstead and Mr. Potter, owner of the *Commercial,* gave a banquet in Thad's honor to which all the civic leaders were invited.

The dinner plodded along until eleven o'clock. Thad was sick of rich food, social chatter, anxious to be on his way. But he rose gamely to his feet to make the expected after-dinner speech.

"I am reminded," he said in opening, "of a remark once made by Admiral Farragut. He swore that dinners he was forced to eat in ports around the world held more terrors than ever his battles had."

In the midst of the laughter, a member of Thad's crew slipped in to tell him the weather had cleared. Thad told the man to see that inflation of the *Enterprise* was begun at once. Then he excused himself and, with Halstead and Potter, slipped away.

From the office of the *Commercial,* Thad telegraphed Professor Henry that he was about to embark, while Halstead ordered the special flight edition of the paper run off. Thaddeus would not wait for the papers nor even take time to change from his banquet clothes. He wished to supervise the inflation which was well under way when they reached the field.

Not long after he and Halstead arrived on the field a messenger brought the newspapers and a wire from Professor Henry:

FAIR WEATHER PREVAILING EAST TO THE COAST. GOOD LUCK!

By 3 a.m. the *Enterprise* was tugging at her mooring ropes. Several banqueters had gathered to watch the ascension. They came bearing delicacies from the banquet table, and a jug of hot coffee which they had wrapped in a blanket.

"Might come in handy," one insisted. "Never know where you might land."

Thaddeus dwarfed the passenger basket as he pulled himself into it. The tall figure in top hat and frock coat looked weird in the flickering light from flares held by the spectators. A light breeze blew from the east. Conditions were perfect.

Murat Halstead was still bemoaning the fact he could not go along when Thad raised his hand, then dropped it in the signal to free him. A cheer rose with the *Enterprise* as she shot up into the darkness.

CHAPTER EIGHT

BEYOND BLUE RIDGE

The *Enterprise* surged this way and that as it ascended. Doubters gleefully reported later that Professor Lowe was last seen flying west. Actually the balloon was swallowed in darkness before it had risen more than a few hundred feet.

Thaddeus continued to drop ballast until his craft caught the easterly current he sought. The raised figures on the barometer told him he had reached 7000 feet. The thermometer was at 0°.

An odd tap-tapping started inside the gas envelope, as if it held trapped hundreds of tiny woodpeckers. Thaddeus realized immediately that the swift ascent from the damp warmth of an Ohio April to the midwinter temperature at this altitude had congealed the moisture in the gas. A fine, glassy bead-like hail was falling on the silk inside the bag and rolling down the neck of the balloon. Miniature snow storms often took place within the gas envelope for the same reason.

The neck of the balloon was always kept open during flight so it could "blow off" as the airship rose and the gas expanded. A bushel or so of the tiny frozen particles were discharged through the opening, causing the *Enterprise* to shoot upwards once more.

Thaddeus' fingers on the barometer told him he was now at 14,000 feet. During the process, the balloon had again been tossed about and driven off course, but now he was riding eastward once more.

Although the balloon was racing through space with extreme rapidity, the candle Thad lit to write his log needed no protection. He tore several sheets from his note-book and let them fall from his hand. They dropped to the floor of the balloon without a flutter and lay still. Thad knew he had no sense of motion because his aircraft was floating in, as well as with, the air stream, yet the phe-nomenon never ceased to amaze him.

Below, the dark mass of earth was pinpointed by an occa-sional light bobbing along as a farmer went out to milk his cows. The first rays of sun picked up the gold of early hay, and glinted off the leaves of seemingly endless forests. The air was cold and clear.

Thaddeus, who had never tasted wine nor cared to, knew the feeling of real intoxication. He shouted and sang with the joy of flight! Surprised birds gave him a wide berth, and he called out to them as to fellow mariners in a private sea.

The sun itself looked like a disc of burnished copper as it rose over the rugged peaks of the Blue Ridge Moun-tains. Thad estimated them to be about 100 miles away. Beyond, he glimpsed the sea. One peak seemed to be rising right out of the ocean.

As the sun's full heat struck the *Enterprise,* the gas ex-panded, boosting the balloon to 16,000 feet. Now the yel-low plains of Ohio gave way to rolling green as he ap-proached the foothills. The snowy peaks ahead took on a menacing quality as if they could reach out and pull his fragile balloon against their craggy sides.

Dumping ballast to avoid the mountains he shot well above them, but noted he was drifting south. Once clear, however, he was sure he could regain his easterly current.

The pine covered slopes below looked soft as a featherbed but above timber line the rocky cliffs and deep chasms covered only by scrubby growth appeared hard and unyielding as spikes.

Riding just above a gorge, he suddenly felt as though a giant claw had reached out to grab his balloon and pull it down. Desperately his hands sought the sandbags he used for ballast, but before he grasped one he was projected violently upwards. Looking out he saw the rounded bald dome of a mountain top so close he could almost touch it.

Thaddeus became more angry than afraid as the fickle drafts turned his aircraft into an unmanageable monster. Then suddenly his wild ride was over. The mountains were behind him and he was descending rapidly toward a hillside. He realized with astonishment that he had been pushed as high as 22,000 feet, and fallen a mile a minute, yet still had had no sense of motion.

The vision of himself as a long-legged lad walking a frozen New Hampshire road rose before his mind's eye.

"Someday I shall fly right over the mountains," the boy had said.

Then he had laughed at his bold dream. Now it was done.

To one side of the hill he was approaching were several plowmen in a field. Thaddeus hovered just above their heads. Picking up his megaphone he called:

"What state is this?"

The plowmen looked around. Seeing no one they went back to their work. Thaddeus repeated his question louder:

"What state is this?"

Again they looked about. Still seeing nobody, one of the men shouted "Virginia" in the general direction of a clump of trees.

Satisfied, Thaddeus decided to push on to the coast. Picking up several bags of sand ballast he began to throw them out one by one. The first one landed quite close to the fieldhands, who took a startled look upwards and fled for their lives.

Thad roared with laughter. The incident provided relief from the tension caused by his trip over the Blue Ridge.

The *Enterprise* rose obediently and continued to float in a southeasterly direction for another hour. Thad let out a shout of triumph. The Atlantic Ocean shimmered just ahead. He had won his goal. Glancing at his chronometer he saw it was just 10 a.m. In seven hours he had flown all the way from Cincinnati to the coast, over 600 miles. Despite the mountains, he must have averaged 100 miles per hour.

He was over marshy ground in which men were working at some crop Thad decided must be rice. He descended again to look over the ground for a good landing spot. This time the men watched with interest as he approached, and waved in a friendly fashion. Thad waved back but after a few minutes decided to return inland to higher, dryer ground before landing.

Again he threw out a sandbag in order to gain altitude. As he floated up and away, he noticed one of the younger men studying the bag he had dropped. Then the lad started chasing after him, shouting, and Thad leaned over the side of the basket to catch his words.

"Hello, Mister," the words wafted up to Thad's incredulous ears. "I reckon you dropped your baggage."

For half an hour the *Enterprise* bobbed along quite close to the ground, in a southwesterly direction, until Thaddeus saw a clearing near a field of cotton. Again he started to land. He had barely touched the ground when he heard shouts, and looking round, was confronted with an onrushing army of planters and field hands. Wielding every kind of farm implement, they seemed bent on hacking him and his balloon to pieces.

He rose into the air, leaving the men to shake their weapons. Just ahead was a barren ridge covered with scrubby pitch pine. A rickety looking settlement sprawled to the south of it. The ridge appeared to be inhabited only by birds, who took off squawking as he approached.

It seemed as good a place as he would find to land, as land he must, since the *Enterprise* had little lifting power left. His supply of sandbags was exhausted. Seeing people working on the hill's slope, he threw out his anchor which caught in a rail fence and called to them to help him. The spectacle of him dropping from the sky startled them so they watched open-mouthed, apparently rooted with the vegetables they had been cultivating.

As Thaddeus jumped from the basket and proceeded to moor his aircraft himself, a woman fully six feet tall approached and offered to help him. He handed her one of the ropes to hold while he valved out the remaining gas. The others who had closed in a circle around him, grimaced and held their noses as the evil smelling coal gas filled the air. Otherwise they were silent and watchful.

The stillness took on an ominous quality, enhanced by a stack of shotguns Thad spied beneath the rail fence. Realizing he must be an awesome sight to these simple folk, dressed as he was in top hat and long black frock coat, he decided to prove he was not the devil they doubtless thought him.

He offered them food and delicacies, but they backed away. He showed them his water bottles in which the liquid was frozen solid, and explained to them where he had been and how cold it was. Then, from heavy blanket wrappings, he took the large thermos of coffee, as hot as when it was first poured.

At once Thad knew he had made a mistake. The circle of people fell back again, eyes round with fear. Surely this was the devil himself if he could produce ice and boiling coffee from the same basket.

Then an old man pushed to the front of the crowd and shook his fist in Thad's face.

"Only a Yankee could do a thing like that," he shouted. Then turning to the crowd. "He must be shot on the spot where he dropped from the skies."

There was a murmur of approval. But the young woman who had been standing all the while beside Thaddeus reassured him.

"Most of them are cowards," she declared, loud enough for them to hear. "All the brave men of the neighborhood have gone to war." Then turning to the others: "We'll take him to Unionville to the authorities," she commanded.

Two men were dispatched for a wagon. The woman was the only one who dared help Thad with his equipment. The sight of his oddly shaped instruments was enough to make the others keep their distance.

Finally gas bag, basket, instruments, and balloonist were stowed in a huge farm wagon drawn by six mules. The crowd followed at a distance as they jogged toward the village Thad had noticed earlier.

The woman led him into a log hut where she stirred up the fire and started to prepare supper although it was only 3 o'clock in the afternoon. Meanwhile she informed Thaddeus that he was on the border between North and South Carolina. The height on which he had landed was called Pea Ridge.

"Peas," she told him, "are the only thing that will grow in such barren soil."

When everything was ready, the woman called out and several people pushed into the one small room. They sat down on three-legged stools around a table fashioned from a split pine trunk. From a Dutch oven near the fireplace she drew a tray of rich golden brown cakes the size and shape of goose eggs which she described as "corn dodgers."

"I'm sorry there's no butter nor nuthin'," she apologized.

"That's cause of old Abe Lin-korn's gunboats," one of the men volunteered. "There's no butter, nor bacon nor coffee. But we got good ole Louisiana molasses." He grinned, handing Thad a huge jug.

Thad excused himself and went out to the cart to bring back several jars of preserves, happy, at last, to find use for the delicacies that had been forced upon him.

Immediately after dinner, Thaddeus was invited to get back into the wagon. A committee had been chosen to take him and his gear to the authorities in Unionville. From the multitude that followed the wagon, Thad decided the whole town was the committee.

The ride to Unionville in the springless wagon was the longest he had ever endured. By the time they approached the town he was covered with dust and he could count every joint in his body. It was nearly 10 p.m. and he had had no sleep for forty hours.

In the gas-lit streets he noted that most of his followers were still with him. Sleepily he pondered on which looked most outlandish, he in his rumpled dusty frock coat and tall silk hat, or that wild-eyed mob with their long sandy hair and beards, loping along in their dirty blue jeans and crumpled slouch hats.

Thaddeus was surprised when they halted in front of

the inn instead of the jail. Several of the men escorted him inside, still carrying his precious instruments. They were met by a rotund little innkeeper.

"I am Professor Thaddeus Sobieski Coulincourt Lowe," Thad announced in his most impressive tones, "engaged in scientific research. I have just landed my balloon on Pea Ridge, and these folks have been kind enough to bring me and my equipment into town."

"He's a Yankee spy, that's what," one of the men muttered. "But the jailhouse's closed so we brung him here."

The innkeeper reacted oddly. He approached quite close to Thad, raising his oil lamp, and peered at him nearsightedly. "Can it be—is it possible. . . ? Well, my, my, my!"

Suddenly, reaching into his pocket, the host began handing out silver coins to Thad's guard.

"All right, all right," he cried pushing them towards the door. "Put the balloon in the barn. Carefully, mind, and there's a shot of likker for each if no harm comes to it." He made shooing motions with his pudgy hands. "I'll take care of the Professor. You can go along now."

When the last man was out in the street and the door tightly closed, the man turned to Thaddeus, throwing wide his arms.

"Professor Lowe! It is you, indeed. What an honor, what an honor! But what an unfortunate time for you to visit us. Those ignorant fools might have shot you."

"Oh come now, surely this talk of rebellion's not that serious." Thad sank wearily into a chair. "Forgive me, but whom do I have the pleasure . . ?

"Name's Fant, Professor. I saw you make a cable ascension a year ago in Charleston. What a sight! I could never forget such an event—nor the man who performed so daring a feat! But come, you must be empty as a drum. We'll talk while you eat."

Fant was frankly incredulous when Thaddeus described his trip. Finally Thad drew out from a roll of blankets a copy of the *Commercial* he had carried with him. Fant took it gingerly.

"This is Abolitionist literature, Professor. You could be hung for having it. Better keep it hidden." Then seeing Lowe's expression. "You Yankees don't seem to realize the South means business. We intend to show the Federals they cain't push us around, beggin' your pahdon, sir."

The little man took on a pompous dignity as he spoke. Thaddeus had no doubt he meant every word.

"Well, it's just to prove I left Cincinnati today."

Fant studied the date on the paper—April 20, 1861. Then he examined his fingers. They were marked with wet ink.

"You left Cincinnati at 3 a.m. and landed on Pea Ridge at just after noon?"

Thaddeus nodded.

"Why, that means you traveled some 900 miles in nine hours. It's not possible!"

"Well, I did," said Thaddeus wearily. "And now I'm going to fly the Atlantic."

"Yes? Well—yes, of course you are." Fant was suddenly reassuring and very solicitous, thinking perhaps that the altitude had affected Thad's mind. "But first you've got to get some rest, Professor. We may still have a parcel of trouble over this spy business you know. You'll need to have your wits about you."

Thaddeus heartily agreed.

CHAPTER NINE

FIRST PRISONER OF WAR

Thaddeus rolled over and groaned. His face and hands felt like huge boils, and his ears cringed from the incessant knocking at the door. It seemed as if he had just gone to sleep.

With effort, he opened his stinging eyes. The room was early morning gray. Another sound invaded his consciousness; a low mumbling rose from outside the window, as if a swarm of bumble bees had gathered there.

The knocking became more insistent, accompanied now by the excited voice of his host calling:

"Professor Lowe. Professor Lowe. Wake up and let me in!"

Thaddeus dragged himself to the door, feeling his face tenderly.

"I thought you understood I did not wish to be disturbed," he said as the tubby innkeeper bustled in.

"I tried to send them away, Professor. But there were so many, I was afraid they'd break down the door. When the sheriff came, and Mr. Thomsen, I had to . . ." Fant broke off, holding his lantern close to Thad. "Oh, sir, your face!" he cried.

Thaddeus turned and peered into the glass over the washstand. Even in the dim light he could see his face was so swollen and red it was hardly recognizable. His hands too were puffy and discolored, and they felt stiff when he tried to work the fingers.

"It's just a bad sun- and wind-burn," Thad said impatiently, striding to the window and pulling up the blind. "What's going on, a fair or something?"

Below him in the square in front of the inn was a mass of people, jostling and mumbling. Someone caught sight of Thad when the shade went up, and let out a roar.

"There he is. There's the damyankee spy!"

All eyes were raised. Some fists were shaking. Thad quickly lowered the blind and turned back to Fant.

"You see how it is, Professor." Fant was apologetic. "Most those folks ain't never seen a real Yankee. The sheriff and Mr. Thomsen are downstairs. You'd better talk with them."

"And who is Mr. Thomsen?" Thad was less fearful of the mob outside than affronted at this invasion of his privacy.

"Mr. Thomsen is a member of the legislature—very influential—" Fant's voice was hushed with deference.

Thad sighed and looked longingly at the warm featherbed. "Tell 'em I'll be right down."

He made his usual careful toilet before meeting the delegation in the inn parlor.

"Your servant, sir," one gentleman stepped out from the group but did not proffer his hand.

"Why am I honored with this early morning visit?" Thad emphasized the word "early."

"I sincerely regret that your rest has been disturbed, Professor—ah—ah . . ."

"Lowe. Thaddeus S. C. Lowe."

"Ah, yes. Professor Lowe. I am Mr. Thomsen of the

South Carolina legislature. May I present the sheriff of Unionville."

Three or four other men were introduced to Thad. They bowed politely but none offered to shake his hand. Mr. Thomsen went directly to the point.

"You realize, Professor, that a state of war exists between South Carolina, as a member of the Confederate States of America, and the Federal Union. As a Yankee, you are an enemy of the Confederacy. Your entry into enemy territory was made in a manner so unusual as to lead our citizenry to assume your intentions may not be friendly."

"But that's absurd," cried Thaddeus. "I can easily prove that my motives in making this flight into so-called 'enemy' territory are purely scientific. Besides, my 'unusual' manner of entry, could hardly be called unobtrusive."

"All that will be decided in session later on," Thomsen replied. "Right now I must ask you to step into my carriage. Our good people outside want a look at a real Yankee."

When Thad protested being put on exhibition, Mr. Thomsen and the sheriff took his arms and walked him to the door. For three hours they drove him through the streets while Thad became angrier and hungrier. The crowds gaped, yelled a few derisive remarks, finally wandered off.

Back at the inn, Fant had prepared a splendid breakfast for his distinguished guests. Their hunger satisfied, Mr. Thomsen questioned Thad closely. Finally Thad fetched copies of the *Commercial* from their hiding place in the folds of his balloon to prove that his one-man invasion of the Confederacy had no warlike purpose.

Mr. Thomsen was grave as he read the account of Thad's flight plans and proposed Atlantic journey, warning Thad again that the possession of Abolitionist literature was punishable by death.

"I had no idea we were actually at war," Thad told him. "The secession of the southern states is considered in the North an ill-advised act of rebellion against the Federal Union, which our government hopes to put an end to peaceably and swiftly."

"In that case, I'm afraid Yankeeland is in for a big surprise," Thomsen replied grimly.

He was finally convinced Thad had not entered his fair state for the purpose of spying, and signed a certificate of free conduct home.

"But there are no trains out of Unionville on Sunday," Thomsen told him. "My wife and I would be honored if you would take dinner with us."

After dinner, Mrs. Thomsen took Thad walking in her garden. Pointing out a special plot of vegetables, she said they were for her son, in service and on his way to Manassas Junction.

"It's difficult to get fresh vegetables to him," she explained, "but when we take Washington, it won't be necessary any more." She spoke as of a practically accomplished fact.

Monday morning Thad found that direct train service north to Washington no longer existed. He must go south to Columbia and get transportation from there through the Confederate west.

It took six hours to cover the sixty miles to the capital. It was mid-afternoon when Thad slung his long unwieldy barometer in its canvas case across his shoulders, clutched his other instruments in his arms, and hurried down the platform.

In the office of the Adams Express Company, he arranged

for the transportation of the *Enterprise* to Cincinnati. As he stepped from the office, he heard someone shout:

"There he goes! That's the fellow with the gun on his back and the infernal machines in his hands."

A big man with a black beard grabbed Thad's arm.

"You'd better come along with me," he growled.

"By whose authority—and why?" demanded Thad, shaking himself free.

"In the name of the law," the man retorted brusquely, flashing a sheriff's badge and revolver. "I arrest you as an enemy of the Confederacy!"

Thad decided to have no words with the officer. A crowd had gathered. It began to rumble ominously as the sheriff pushed Thad into a waiting carriage. The rumble became a roar as the caravan trotted off towards the jail.

"Tar and feather the damyankee!" a strident voice suggested.

"That's too good for him!" screeched another. "Let's hang 'im!"

As they pulled up in front of the jail, angry citizens rocked the carriage. Grasping hands pawed at Thad. The policeman was fumbling in his pockets for change to pay the driver.

"Here, hold these!" Thad shoved his instruments at the sheriff. "I'll pay him myself."

"Now isn't that just like a damyankee!" the sheriff grimaced at the mob—"known for his assurance at any time." Then he hustled Thad to the comparative safety of prison walls.

Curious policemen fingered Thad's delicate instruments while he waited uncomfortably for the mayor, whom the sheriff had summoned. Finally a group of tophatted officials bustled in.

"Mayor W. H. Boatwright, at your service, sir," announced one gentleman.

The city fathers mulled interminably over Thad's credentials and Mr. Thomsen's safe conduct certificate. When Thad could stand the suspense no longer he told the mayor:

"Members of the staff at South Carolina College would remember my name. I have corresponded with several of the faculty there. I'm certain the president himself would vouch for me."

Another lengthy conference ensued as the city council considered Thad's proposition and finally agreed to give him this chance to prove he was no spy.

The college president arrived and proved to be a Fellow of the Smithsonian Institution and a personal friend of Professor Henry.

"I know Professor Lowe well," he declared, "both by reputation and by sight. I saw some of your experiments in Charleston last winter, Professor." He turned to Thad, eager to hear how the plans for the Atlantic voyage were progressing. The brotherhood of science proved stronger than political considerations.

When Thaddeus was finally chugging westward, his certificate and pass duly signed by Mayor Boatwright, he felt somewhat like Alice when she emerged from Wonderland. In the past two days he had been wined and dined and threatened with hanging in such quick succession he was dizzy. At no time had he a moment to assess the value of his rapid flight from Cincinnati to the sea.

The train crept smokily across the western reaches of the Confederacy. During the halting five-day journey, there unfolded before Thad sights and sounds which made him forget his plans for the transatlantic journey.

At every way station bands were playing "The Girl I

Left Behind" or "Dixie"—not the familiar patriotic songs, like "Yankee Doodle," that had been the musical backdrop of Thad's northern upbringing.

Young men in new gray uniforms, carrying an assortment of firearms, piled onto the coach at each stop, as girls and women waved goodbye from the platform. Some of the ladies carried little flags—strange, foreign flags with an insolent pattern of stars and bars.

Passengers were shuttled back and forth among the coaches or disembarked entirely to make room for these brawny men who had suddenly become soldiers. To Thad, the spectacle was unbelievable, distressing yet compelling. Mathematical calculations as to the number of troops he saw under arms and of recruits flooding into the posts produced staggering results. Thad became convinced he was witness to a total population preparing for war.

As the train chugged hesitantly across Tennessee, top-hatted gentlemen boarded the train at each stop. They were, Thad learned, members of the legislature which had been called to Nashville in special session to vote on secession.

His own formal garb acted as a "silk hat" passport. He accompanied the group off the train at Nashville, attended several of their meetings, and thus was present when Tennessee seceded from the Union.

Now a sense of urgency gripped him. He hurried to catch the first train to Louisville, Kentucky, where he boarded an Ohio River ferry for Cincinnati.

As the boat nosed into its berth on the Ohio side, the rising sun glinted on the stars and stripes whipping above the dock. A thankful shout arose from the group of "Yankees" on the ferry's deck, returning home from a land no longer part of their own.

It was April 27th, exactly one week since Thaddeus had left Cincinnati. When his feet once more touched United States soil, his course of action was already clear in his mind, his decision made.

He hurried first to the nearest telegraph office and wired the President of the action he had witnessed in the Tennessee legislature. Then he went to the office of the *Commercial.*

"That serious is it?" said Halstead when he heard Thad's story. "No wonder we didn't hear news of you."

"Always thought this rebellion was no tempest in a teapot," fumed Potter. "Don't believe Washington thinks so either. The people are too complacent. Got to wake them up!"

"Anyway, your flight was a success," recalled Halstead. "But how will the war affect your plans for the Atlantic crossing?"

"There's more important work for me now," Thad replied. "The army can use my balloons. They'd be the eyes of the troops! Give us a terrific advantage! Maybe save lives—even shorten the war!"

Murat Halstead needed little convincing as to the potential of an aeronautic corps.

"I'll do all I can to help you," he assured Thad. "The Secretary of the Treasury, Salmon Chase, is an old friend of mine. I'll send a letter to him immediately."

Thad decided the quickest, cheapest way home was to fly. However, adverse winds blew him off course. He was forced to land in Hamilton, Ontario. Canada was celebrating Queen Victoria's birthday, so Thad replenished his funds with exhibitions, then continued home by rail.

The delay made his reunion with his family all too brief. A telegram from Washington already awaited him there.

After the first joyous moments Leontine asked apprehensively:

"What is it, Thaddeus?"

"It is from Secretary Salmon P. Chase, my dear. He wishes me to present myself and my balloon in Washington at my earliest possible convenience."

Leontine sat quietly for a moment, rocking little Ava Eugenie's cradle. Thad had written from Cincinnati a long account of his journey and something of his plans, so the message was not a surprise.

Her dark eyes were filled with foreboding as she raised them to his face.

CHAPTER TEN

A TELEGRAM FOR THE PRESIDENT

Washington was in an uproar when Thad arrived on June 5th, 1861. From his train window he saw tent cities everywhere. The streets were full of jostling people. The scattering of women eyed him boldly; officials and officers hurried back and forth, and men—thousands of them—in the varied uniforms of regiments from Maine to Ohio, strolled and gawked like holiday sightseers.

These were the factory workers, shopkeepers, farmer boys, the patriotic volunteers led by lawyers and politicians as green as themselves. This was the three-month militia called up by the President to "suppress combinations against the government."

Again a sense of urgency prodded Thad as he made his way through the cocky crowds to the National Hotel. If these untrained citizens were the Union's answer to the determined Rebels already approaching Washington, they would need his balloons, indeed every advantage they could muster.

By the end of May, Confederate pickets had been spotted within sight of the capital. Federal troops clogged every bridge across the Potomac. The soft spring air was filled with dust, the shouts of wagoners, the rumble and clatter of wheels and hooves. Shovels tore at the fragrant Virginia earth as the soldiers dug breastworks across the flowering countryside.

Thad dropped his baggage at the hotel and hurried to the office of Treasury Secretary Chase. The Secretary greeted Thad warmly.

"Our friend Murat Halstead claims you're the only aeronaut in the country capable of heading an effective air corps. But you've plenty of competition. Five other aeronauts are clamoring for the job."

Chase motioned Thad to be seated and eased himself into his desk chair.

"No one can get close to the Chief of Staff, General Winfield Scott. Our 'grand old man' is a great military organizer with 50 years of service behind him. But," the Secretary sighed, "he's a sick old man! Can't be made to see the need for anything new. As for aeronautics—Phut!"

Thad could see that Mr. Chase was more discouraged with the military setup than he cared to admit.

"The President, on the other hand," Chase continued, "is enthusiastic about an air arm. I'll try to arrange a meeting for you with Mr. Lincoln."

Thad was exultant as he hurried toward the Smithsonian. He went over and over in his mind how best to convince the President that he was the man to head an aeronautic corps.

His old friend, Professor Henry, seconded Chase. "General Scott is so harrassed with building a military machine, why—pshaw! It's difficult even to get his attention."

"What's been done to make him pay attention?" asked Thad.

Professor Henry shrugged his shoulders. "Not much. The Allen brothers from Providence have been here since April. Their aeronautics are sound enough, far as they go. Same is true of the Dutchman, John Steiner. Of course your friends Wise and La Mountain have thrown their weight around a good deal—"

"Well, then . . ." Thad interjected eagerly. Perhaps he was not too late after all.

Henry held up his hand. "But they're in action, old balloons and all. The Allens are on their way to Falls Church to join Burnside's Brigade and La Mountain is at Fortress Monroe. The navy yard rigged up a sort of balloon carrier to transport him and his gear down the bay."

Thad paced Henry's dark little office in irritation. "I suppose by acting independently under any general they can get to sponsor them, they hope to prove the need for balloons. But with old equipment, outworn operating methods, why, they may do more harm than good. Are they getting paid for their services?"

"I doubt it," was the quick reply.

"And how are they inflating their balloons?"

Henry tipped back in his chair, pleased to see Thad put on his mettle. Now, he was thinking, maybe the army would get the well-organized aeronautic corps he felt it needed. He answered Thad's question quietly.

"They are inflating their balloons at Washington street mains and enlisting what help they can to tow them to the front lines."

Thad exclaimed impatiently. "It's a wonder they haven't destroyed themselves and their aircraft already! Towing an inflated balloon is clumsy at best, but with a crew of amateurs . . !"

"Both La Mountain and Wise have submitted plans for a portable generator," Professor Henry observed, "so balloons could be inflated in the field. But their contraptions would be cumbersome as well as impossibly expensive to make or operate."

"I've been going over in my mind how to make one light, compact, and inexpensive," Thad said, thoughtfully pulling his mustache. "But my first job is to sell Thaddeus Lowe to the United States Army!"

So Thad set up his apparatus on the Smithsonian grounds and began making daily ascensions. He hoped to interest prominent government and army men in his methods by taking them aloft. Experience as a showman had taught him that one practical demonstration was worth a million words.

From the swaying basket of his balloon, suspended half a mile above Washington, he could see through his telescope the Federal fortifications that arced across the fields of Virginia from Chain Bridge south to Alexandria. Close by, the Capitol dome undergoing major repairs, lay open to his view. He could almost look down into the rotunda. Blocks of marble and other debris lay scattered about as if it had been bombarded.

Directly below, and as far as he could see in either direction, the Mall was dotted with tents. Soldiers marched and wheeled, and marched again in an interminable modern war dance.

True to his word, Secretary Chase arranged a meeting with President Lincoln for the evening of June 11th. Professor Henry accompanied Thad to the White House where they found Secretary of War Cameron and General Scott sipping coffee with the President in his study.

The tall Chief Executive was as ugly as Thad had been led to expect. Yet there was beauty in the brooding quality of the craggy face. Despite Lincoln's quiet manner, Thad was aware of a strength and magnetism he had never felt before in any man.

It was immediately obvious that the President was extremely tired. Thad wasted no words.

"I could only appear vain and egotistical if I try to tell you my qualifications are superior to those of my rivals," Thad told the President. "With your permission I prefer to make several practical demonstrations."

Lincoln nodded. "What do you have in mind?"

"I would like to take telegraphic equipment aloft to show you how I propose to transmit speedy reports from my point of observation to ground troops during battle. From the air, I could see enemy movements hidden from anyone on the ground, even a few yards away, by trees, stone walls, and other obstructions. I need not point out the advantage such intelligence would give our forces."

The President was watching Thad from under shaggy brows, assessing him. He grunted approval. Secretary of War Cameron was listening attentively. General Scott wheezed testily.

"Then I would like to make a free flight over enemy installations to prove the value of aircraft in reconnaissance. I'll let you know what the Rebels ate for breakfast."

Lincoln chuckled. His own sense of humor was keen.

"It takes a trained eye to observe detail from any altitude, you understand," Thad continued. "Not long ago one of my colleagues took a young lady up who had never been aloft before. At something over 1000 feet she cried:

" 'Look there. Someone has spilled a load of potatoes and they're rolling all over the road.'

"My fellow aeronaut looked where she was pointing. Consider, sir, his amusement to see that her potatoes were, in fact, a herd of sheep disturbed by something and running back and forth in the lane!"

The President was charmed. "That's a good one, eh, General?"

A snore that ended in what sounded suspiciously like a belch was General Scott's answer. He was dozing comfortably, hands folded over his paunchy stomach.

"Looks like you've bored the General, Professor Lowe," said Lincoln, rising to end the interview. "But don't get cocky about that. It's easy to do. Now then, what will you need for your first demonstration?"

"Besides the telegraphic equipment," replied Thad, "I'll need an operator, a crew to help inflate and launch the balloon. . . ."

"And money?"

"Two hundred and fifty dollars should do it."

The President gave Cameron a personally signed authorization to supply Professor Lowe with all his needs. In a week everything was ready.

News that a telegram would be sent from the aircraft to the White House spread fast. When the *Enterprise* rose above the Smithsonian that clear June morning, Thad could see crowds in the streets below as far as the White House on one side and the Capitol on the other.

Picking up his telescope, Thad examined the entrenchments across the Potomac. Then his gaze swept in an arc around the city.

In the passenger basket with Thad was Herbert Robinson, operator in charge of telegraphic equipment loaned by the American Telegraph Company. A half-mile of fine wire followed the balloon's anchor rope to the ground.

"Are you ready to send?" Thad asked Robinson.

"Ready to send," was the reply.

Slowly Thad dictated:

Balloon *Enterprise*
Washington, D.C.
June 18, 1861

To the President of the United States:

Sir: This point of observation commands an area nearly 50 miles in diameter. The city with its girdle of encampments presents a superb scene. I have pleasure in sending you this first dispatch ever telegraphed from an aerial station and in acknowledging indebtedness for your encouragement for the opportunity of demonstrating the availability of the science of aeronautics in the service of the country.

T. S. C. Lowe

The ground station replied that reception was perfect. The two men remained aloft over an hour sending messages crackling across the wires to Arlington, Virginia, and even as far as Philadelphia. Robinson shared Thad's excitement, pronouncing the event an historical advance in communications.

Thad himself was overjoyed at the success of his demonstration—the first wired message from air to earth. He hoped it would be followed by many sent by him.

A personal note of congratulations from Abraham Lincoln awaited Thad when he reached the ground. He was requested to call on the President that evening to discuss further plans for an air corps.

It was close to morning when Lincoln received Thad alone in his private study. Despite the hour, his interest never flagged, as Thad outlined his plans in detail.

Next day Thad went to the War Department armed with a letter of approval from Mr. Lincoln himself. General Scott could hardly refuse to see him. He made it clear, however, that he intended to do no more. The aeronaut was not even invited to sit down.

In a manner as pompous and affected as had been described to Thad, he strode to his office window. With a mighty sweep of an arm he roared at his visitor to "have a look" at the problem confronting him.

Thad obediently looked out at the jumbled encampments below.

"I must make an army out of that rabble," growled the General. "Do you think I have time to listen to every mad dreamer that comes to my door?"

"But Mr. Lincoln . . ." protested Thad.

"Ah, Mr. Lincoln! What does he know about military affairs? His nose was stuck fast in his law books while I was out fighting Mexicans and Indians! He asked me to talk to you. Well, I've talked to you. So that's that."

A man of less determination might have been discouraged, but after telling Professor Henry what had occurred, Thad added:

"I am convinced that my system of aeronautics is invaluable to my country. I will not let it go by default!"

"Good," said Professor Henry. "On the basis of your performance here during the last two weeks, of your past work, and the plans you have outlined for military aeronautics, I shall go ahead and make my report to Secretary of War Cameron. It will contain a strong recommendation that you be allowed to form an air corps."

Professor Henry's report, extolling at length Thad's accomplishments and capabilities, was delivered to Secretary Cameron on June 21st. "Mr. Lowe," it concluded, "is well qualified to render service."

That very afternoon Thad received orders from Captain Amiel Whipple of the Topographical Engineers to fill his balloon and bring it with the telegraph apparatus to Arlington, Virginia. At last he was to get near the scene of action!

It was a ticklish business transporting an inflated balloon across Long Bridge and down the narrow highway to Arlington. From his precarious perch in the basket, Thad shouted instructions. One moment of inattention and one of the inexperienced soldiers might fumble with a guy rope, or a sudden gust of wind might knock the balloon against the bridge or hopelessly foul it in the trees. James and Ezra Allen had destroyed their balloon that way only the week before.

It was late the following afternoon before the strange caravan reached Arlington. There they were ordered to proceed to Fall's Church. They marched silently through the night, the balloon bobbing like a portly ghost just above the treetops.

At 4 a.m., they reached the Alexandria and London Railroad. Guards warned them against proceeding farther since they were the last Union outpost. Thad decided to make his own observation. By the uncertain dawn light he discovered no Rebel pickets in the vicinity, so he decided to proceed two miles to Bailey's Crossroads.

He found that village in a state of high excitement. A Rebel cavalry unit occupying the vicinity had been frightened away by the approaching balloon. Apparently they assumed that a large Union force accompanied it.

Thaddeus remained near Falls Church five busy days. General Tyler, commander of the First Division that occupied the area, went aloft several times and had an officer sketch an aerial map of the terrain. Captain Whipple, who ascended often, finally became convinced that the balloon might be of practical service in battle.

But the painstaking report Thad prepared for him, estimating costs and outlining proposed operating methods, was turned down.

"We are starting with a limited budget," Captain Whipple explained. "Eventually we may need four balloons with a portable generator for each as you point out. Right now your colleague, John Wise, is prepared to take the field with his present aircraft, and provide a generator for some $200 less than your estimate."

Thad was appalled. "Wise plans to use his old balloon under battle conditions?"

"He is preparing the *Atlantic* for combat now," Whipple replied. "With your experience I'm sure he would consider you a valuable assistant."

"Why, I would not trust myself in Wise's flimsy wornout aerostat!" Thad sputtered. "Nor have I confidence in the man any more! He hasn't had a new idea in twenty years—has no conception of the military requirements of modern warfare."

Unable to say more, Thad picked up his hat and stalked out.

Professor Henry was reassuring. "I've seen Wise's plans for a gas generator. It will be unwieldy and expensive. Doubtless he's stalling for time, hoping you'll give up. But he can't offer what you have for twice the price."

Placing his arm around Thad's shoulders, he led him to a window facing the White House.

"Several times a day I see Mr. Lincoln come to his office window and look down here to see what's going on. I believe you still have him behind you, as well as Chase, Cameron—and me. You can't give up now."

Thad spread his hands in a gesture of helplessness. "How

can I fight the red tape, Joseph? Whipple seems to have the final word."

Professor Henry stared out the window thoughtfully. Finally he turned to Thad.

"Whipple knows nothing about aeronautics. Maybe he's in for a bitter lesson. Let"s hope he learns it before it's too late."

CHAPTER ELEVEN

BETWEEN THE LINES

The July sun turned Washington into a massive dust bowl. From the air, the capital was barely visible beneath its powdery veil kicked up by thousands of marching feet.

Regiment after regiment passed through the city and across the bridges to Virginia. A few wore the new blue uniform of the Federal Army, many more still wore their colorful regimentals. There were the Fire Zouaves in baggy white pants and red fezzes, the 79th New York in bright tartans, the Garibaldi Guards in rakish feathered caps.

They marched to martial music. The battle cry: "On to Richmond" rang in the streets. Congress and the public clamored for action while the three-month militia grew restless as they neared the end of their term. They were eager to get the war done and go home, yet wanted, too, tales of valor to tell their womenfolk.

No one doubted that the Rebels would disperse at the first show of strength—no one, that is, except the officers in the field.

The Army of the Potomac, commanded by General Irvin McDowell, braced to attack Confederate positions across Bull Run, only 23 miles from the Federal capital. While at Confederate headquarters in Manassas Junction, three miles west of the Run, General G. T. Beauregard studied to outmaneuver his West Point classmate and seize Washington.

Irvin McDowell knew only too well the adversary he faced.

"I have hardly one full brigade I can trust to be steady in the line!" he confided to Thad one day as they soared 1000 feet above Washington. "And half of them are armed with old-fashioned smoothbored muskets! We'll need the advantage your balloon observations would give us."

"I just hope you'll have that advantage," Thad replied ruefully. "If you don't, it won't be for lack of effort on my part."

The balloon was settling gently to earth.

"I'll speak to Whipple again about it," McDowell promised as he jumped out.

Thad returned to his hotel that evening to find a happy surprise awaiting him. When he entered his room, a pair of tiny hands covered his eyes. The familiar scent of lavendar revealed the welcome presence of his beloved Leontine. In a moment she was in his arms.

"But you should not have traveled alone," Thad remonstrated. "Secessionists are sabotaging the trains in Maryland! And a beautiful woman with all those soldiers. . . !"

"Oh, but I had an escort," Leontine interrupted—"a very handsome gentleman!"

"Well now," exclaimed Thad, "that could be even more disturbing."

Leontine laughed at his concern. "Come, then and meet this rival. He is waiting to dine with us."

Leontine's escort was none other than Murat Halstead, traveling to Virginia to cover the war for the *Cincinnati Commercial.*

"Business brought me by way of Philadelphia," the editor explained. "I seized the opportunity to call on the charming wife and family you spoke of so often."

When Thad heard his friend was to join the army the following day, he sighed:

"Everyone is moving to the front except me."

"You'll have your fill of war before this is over," Halstead assured him. "We all will."

The following week of July 8th passed with no sign of the predicted attack. Nor did John Wise appear in Washington with his balloon. He still had not arrived on the 16th when General McDowell advanced his army to Centreville, only three miles from Bull Run.

At the approach of the Federal force, Confederate pickets quietly retired behind the natural barrier of the steepsided Run where Beauregard's army had every ford and bridge heavily guarded.

Thus the two giants, squared off for battle, faced each other and waited, while excitement mounted to hysteria in Washington.

Still John Wise did not appear. Thaddeus occupied himself mending frayed ropes and patching the balloon fabric, especially reinforcing the area around the valve. Finally, he applied an extra coat of varnish, determined to be ready should Whipple send for him in the continued absence of Wise.

Meanwhile he watched with amazement the private carriages going out to Virginia. They carried senators, congressmen, and other civilians, in many cases accompanied by ladies, bent on witnessing the battle about to take place.

On the battle line no holiday mood existed. There were isolated but bloody engagements. McDowell, awaiting additional troops, became certain Beauregard had received re-enforcements, but his agents brought information that was spotty and contradictory. On the 19th and 20th he demanded again that an observation balloon be sent. Captain Whipple finally authorized Thad to take over the task.

Late Saturday afternoon, July 20, inflation of the *Enterprise* was begun. It was half full when Thad heard a shout and looking up saw Wise approaching. The older man waved a wad of official papers in Thad's face and demanded he remove his balloon from the main. Sadly, Thad stood aside and watched the battered *Atlantic* fastened to the gas line.

It was past midnight when Wise waved triumphantly from the basket as he was towed off toward Chain Bridge. Despite the hour, Thad somehow prevailed upon the men to finish inflating his *Enterprise.*

Sunday morning, July 21st, was not far advanced before all Washington knew that a major engagement was taking place near Bull Run. Tension spread with the growing realization of how easily a strong Rebel force might capture the capital.

Thad paced beside his tethered balloon. It was near noon when he received a dispatch from Major Hartman Bache, Whipple's superior in the Topographical Engineers. Wise's balloon had become entangled in trees half way to Centreville and was hopelessly damaged. Professor Lowe was to proceed down the Warrenton Turnpike to make contact with McDowell's army.

Close behind the dispatch rider was a contingent of engineers who were to tow the inflated balloon. They set off across Aqueduct Bridge, past Fort Corcoran towards Falls Church. It was an excessively hot, still day, but even without wind the going was slow, due to overhanging trees. Heavy dust choked the men and stung their eyes.

All afternoon they met isolated squads of soldiers marching away from the battlefield. These men explained they had enlisted for three months and their time was up. Battle or no battle they were going home.

At 4:30 the sounds of gunfire and cannon, which had grown louder as they approached the battlefield, became sporadic. When they entered the village of Falls Church, an ominous quiet prevailed. Although there were several hours of daylight ahead, an officer in charge there ordered Thad to halt.

During the long night, Thad's worst fears were confirmed. Bivouaced beside the road with his men, the tethered balloon moving gently against the sky, he watched glumly an ever increasing number of stragglers going towards Washington.

Near morning it began to rain. The sunless dawn revealed darkening stains of sweat and blood on the soldiers' uniforms. The drizzle caked the dust on them, turning all the colors to a ghostly grey.

They came in groups now, sometimes in a semblance of formation. Many were limping, some had bandaged arms or heads. Others were supporting, even carrying their comrades. They walked quietly, without panic or apparent fear. There was no music now, no jokes nor boasts.

Thaddeus found it impossible to get any information. The men's one objective was to get back to their camps on the Potomac. The few officers with them had no authority to tell Thad whether to stay or go. They said that McDowell was still at Centreville where he had tried to rally his forces.

Thaddeus would have liked to advance until he found McDowell, but he could not move against the avalanche of men. If he so far exceeded orders as to make a free flight, it might ruin his chances ever to work again with the army.

Confederate pursuit seemed certain. Federal pickets were withdrawn from in front of Falls Church on Monday afternoon and Thad had no alternative but to return to Fort Corcoran. There he immediately asked for permission to fly over enemy territory.

On Tuesday he made several ascensions from the fort. He saw remnants of the Union Army still moving east. Scattered Rebel patrols left the Federal soldiers alone.

Perhaps the Rebels are massing for an attack, thought Thad, and pushed his plea. The same fear rankled in official minds. On Wednesday, McDowell, back at his old headquarters in Arlington House, ordered Thad to fly over the lines and observe enemy activity.

Thad floated west on a low air stream following the Warrenton Turnpike to Stone Bridge. The countryside below as far as he could see was devastated as if attacked by fire-breathing locusts.

On a rise in front of him were the ruins of two farmhouses, Stone House and Henry House, surrounded by the debris of battle. This had been the center of action where Confederate and Federal troops had fought viciously back and forth across Henry Hill. Here the Union batteries had held until their commanders and gunners fell beside the guns and the lines disintegrated to right and left.

Now Thad was over Confederate territory. He continued south and west examining their positions. Rebel patrols pointed and stared curiously, but no shot was fired. Nor could he see any massing of troops that would indicate an attack on Washington.

It was late afternoon when Thad rose to catch an easterly current that would waft him back to his own lines. He planned to land at Arlington and report directly to General

McDowell. But Federal troops, seeing the balloon approaching from the west, fired on him when he tried to land.

He was low enough to hear the soldiers shout to show his colors. Thad was baffled. No one had thought to have him carry a flag. Nor could he make the men on the ground understand who he was.

Meanwhile the current was carrying him west again. He realized he would have to land outside the lines.

At dusk he noticed three hills directly in front of him. He had valved so much gas when trying to land he could not fly over them. A clump of trees just beneath him seemed to offer protection from prying eyes. With a heartfelt prayer, Thad floated gently down amongst them.

Apparently the trees hid his descent, for no one approached him. He estimated he was two miles away from his own lines, in territory sympathetic to the South. If he walked back it meant abandoning his precious aircraft, and one of his own pickets might shoot him on sight. Besides he had painfully twisted his ankle jumping from the basket, which had caught in some tree branches and hung several feet above the ground.

Untangling the balloon without injuring it was a slow job. It was dark when he methodically folded the deflated bag, placed it with all the ropes neatly in the basket, and sat down beside it to rest.

It was a fragrant summer evening, and the crickets sang as contentedly as if man had never come to tear their world apart with war. Thad soon dozed off, his head cushioned on the folded balloon cloth.

He was startled awake by the sound of heavily booted feet trampling the underbrush. The sound was all around him. His only chance if it were a Confederate patrol, was to lie still and hope they would miss him in the dark.

"If they're trying to be quiet," Thad thought, "they could certainly take a lesson from the Indians."

Suddenly four men loomed over him. He had no way of knowing whether he was captured or saved till one of them spoke.

"Corporal Dokes, 31st New York Volunteers, at your service, sir." The lad scratched his head. "Your wife said we'd find you right about here. Don't know how she knew. We thought you'd come down south of Arlington, round about Fort Runyon, just by Long Bridge."

"Bless my darling Leontine," Thad thought. She had gone out to Fort Corcoran that morning to visit him and stayed to watch his flight. "No one else in the whole Union Army would have had sense enough to look for me!"

"What's that, sir?"

"No one notified the troops down there about my flight," replied Thad impatiently. "They wouldn't let me land. What's our situation, now?"

"As far as we can tell you're on a farm called Mason's plantation, two and a half miles west and north from Alexandria. The place is crawling with Rebel pickets, but I doubt if they know you're here any more than we did."

"My descent must have been hidden by the trees, and those hills just west of here. But heaven knows how you got through if there are Rebel pickets all around," Thad said wryly. "You were making enough noise to scare a deaf man. Now the problem is to get all this gear out of here. It's too valuable to abandon."

"That little wife of yours has everything figgered out, sir. We'll be back for you in no time." With that they were gone —much more silently, Thad noticed, than they had come.

The "no time" seemed endless to Thad. As the night wore on a fog crept in. He became so uncomfortably damp and chilly that he could not get back to sleep. His ankle throbbed, and he had an overwhelming desire to sneeze.

He did not realize a new day had begun till he saw a figure approaching several feet away. It was not light enough to make out any details but it appeared to be an old woman. The apparition wore a shapeless cotton dress, and a raggy shawl covered her head against the dampness.

Apparently she had not yet seen him. She kept her head low, looking for something on the ground—acorns perhaps, or wood chips to start her fire. If she were short-sighted enough she might pass him right by. Chances were, if she lived hereabouts, she was a Rebel sympathizer, who would turn him right over to the enemy.

At that moment she caught sight of him. Oddly she showed no surprise or fear, but came right over to him, finger on lips.

Except for her strange conduct and some sixth sense, Thad would still not have recognized her. Black hair straggled limply over her face. She even smelled of barn and kitchen. No hint of clean sweet lavender remained.

"My dear," Thad whispered. "You made a terrible mistake in leaving the stage to become a wife and mother. You are a superb actress!"

She laughed softly, then again cautioning silence, disappeared in the shadow of the woods. She reappeared in minutes, gingerly leading a broken down horse and wagon through the trees.

"It was the only way," she explained as they loaded balloon and basket onto the wagon. "The men would have been taking too much of a risk. But who would notice an old hag like me?"

"I would," declared Thad, "and I don't like you taking chances."

"And I don't intend to have my husband hung as a spy. Now get in there with your old balloon and I'll cover you up with this tarpaulin."

Again Thad protested, but Leontine would not listen.

"The pickets automatically question all men," she said. "Women are not as suspect. For that very reason I'm certain plenty are running information through the lines. Come along. We must lose no more time."

Jolting back to the road, cramped and smothering under the heavy covering, Thad recalled his last uncomfortable ride in a farm wagon, when he was taken as a spy to Union, South Carolina. Now his swollen ankle ached unbearably, adding to his misery.

There seemed to be a great deal of traffic on the road for so early in the morning. Each time he heard voices or a horse and wagon pass, he gritted his teeth, fearing for Leontine. Surely they would not hang a woman!

Leontine marched along smartly, dragging the ancient horse and wagon behind her. Confederate pickets paid no more attention to her than they would to any farmer's wife.

Union pickets were on the lookout for them outside the lines.

Thad went immediately to Arlington House to make his report to General McDowell. His news that the enemy showed no sign of pursuit was wired at once to Washington.

For the first time in weeks, McDowell relaxed. Thad amused him with the story of his landing outside the lines and of Leontine's daring rescue. The general laughed heartily at Thad's description of her disguise.

"She's a brave woman, Professor," he assured Thad, "but no better than you deserve. It takes more courage than most have to fly over enemy territory. At least you should be in uniform in case of capture."

McDowell stood up, impatiently thumping the palm of his left hand with his right fist.

"The army should have half a dozen balloons, properly manned and equipped," he declared. "I'm convinced, Lowe, that the results at Bull Run might have been different had we had information from your balloon!"

CHAPTER TWELVE

FIRST WAR BALLOON

The next afternoon, Thad paced General Scott's outer office with a note that President Lincoln had given him the evening before clutched in his hand. Four times he had sent it in to the General who seemingly conferred with everyone else in Washington, later lunched, even napped.

Thad looked again at the little document that should have opened any door.

> Will Lt. General Scott please see Professor Lowe once more about his balloon?
> July 25, 1861
>
> A. Lincoln

With sudden decision, he clamped on his wide-brimmed black hat and marched the short distance from the War Department to the Executive Mansion. Though the anteroom was crowded, Thad was ushered into the President's office between callers.

When Mr. Lincoln heard Thad's story, his solemn face grew more serious.

"Come on," he said. He picked up his shabby silk hat and stalked out of his office. Long-legged as Thad was, he had difficulty keeping up with the former rail splitter as he strode back to the War Department.

The guard swiftly stumbled to attention. "The President

of the United States!" echoed down the corridors as Lincoln made his way directly to General Scott's office.

The old soldier's face showed comic amazement when he found himself confronted by his Commander in Chief.

"General," said the President, "this is my friend, Professor Lowe, who is organizing an aeronautic corps for the army, and is to be its chief. I wish you would facilitate his work in every way."

Mr. Lincoln told his Chief of Staff to write letters to Captain John Dahlgren, Commandant of the Navy Yard, and to Quartermaster General Montgomery C. Meigs, instructing them to supply Thad with all equipment necessary for the Aeronautic Corps on land and water.

On July 29th, Thad received orders from Captain Whipple to be in Arlington, ready for duty, within 24 hours. The Topographical Engineers would provide twenty men to transport the inflated balloon. He would receive $30 a day for his services.

Thad wrote an immediate and violent protest, stating that the *Enterprise* was too old for hard use in the field, too bulky and unmaneuverable for reconnaissance. Besides, it had been damaged by the trees when he made the forced landing in Virginia.

"I would rather work for $10 a day and be allowed to construct a suitable balloon," Thad stated.

Knowing that the enemy was uncomfortably close to Washington, Thad did try to carry out Whipple's orders. But even the weather became party to what seemed a well-laid plan to discredit the idea of an air corps once and for all.

A heavy thunderstorm blew the *Enterprise* into overhanging trees, making it completely unfit. Whipple seized the excuse to give up the whole idea of war balloons again.

This time Thad's patient friend, Joseph Henry, wrote a scathing letter to Whipple's superior, Major Hartman Bache. He demanded that Thaddeus be commissioned to build a suitable balloon, the cost of which would be negligible in view of the benefits.

On August 2nd, 1861, construction of the first war balloon was finally authorized.

The *Eagle* was ready for service on the 28th of August. A small balloon, it was made of the best India silk, with linen network, and guy ropes of manila cordage.

During its construction at his shop in Philadelphia, Thad received $5 per day, but was promised $10 when he went into action. The Army had certainly taken him at his word!

The very day he returned to Washington, Thad received the following dispatch:

> Get silk balloon in readiness for inflation. Detail 30 men to Columbian Armory to aid in inflating and transportation. Enclose order for gas.
>
> J. C. Woodruff
> Major, T. E.
> August 28, 1861

On the morning of August 29th, came another from Whipple at Fort Corcoran:

"General McClellan desires you to be here 3 A.M."

Stalky, barrel-chested George McClellan had replaced the unfortunate McDowell as Commander of the Army of the Potomac. An old friend of Lincoln's from Illinois, he came fresh from victories in West Virginia that had won him the nickname "Little Napoleon."

When Thad made his first ascension in the *Eagle* before

dawn that August morning, he was shocked to see that the Rebels had advanced almost to the gates of Fort Corcoran. Their camp fires glowed on Munson's and Upton's hills, the same hills that had hidden Thad's descent the month before.

Sunlight revealed the Confederate soldiers building breastworks on the hills' sides, and mounting huge batteries. They were so close, Thad felt he was peering right down the muzzles of the cannon.

Thad reported directly to General McClellan.

"I wish you or one of your aides would go aloft," he told the commander. "Some of those batteries look very odd to me."

McClellan himself decided to go up with Thad. He studied the guns for some minutes, then roared with laughter. More than half the heavy "artillery" he pronounced "Quaker guns," constructed of barrels and stove pipes. He drew the reassuring conclusion that the Rebels were not strong enough to storm Washington, and could only try to pin the Union forces to its defense by bluff.

During the next month, Thad made several ascensions each day from Fort Corcoran and from Arlington Heights. The enemy was so close that their bullets whistled through the rigging of his aircraft. The soldiers who had been of the opinion Thad and his balloon were entertainment provided by the government, began to watch the tall frock-coated figure with admiration.

"It takes more guts 'n I'd have to go up there! One bullet in that bag an' he's a goner!"

The generals of McClellan's command were equally impressed, often ascending themselves to make their own reconnaissance. Thad's old friend, McDowell, now commanding the First Corps; handsome, hot-tempered Joe

Hooker; veteran Samuel Heintzelman, still youthful enough in spirit to appreciate a new idea; and McClellan himself; were frequent passengers. All agreed to the need for an effective air corps such as Thad advocated.

Thad had been at Fort Corcoran little more than a week when his Division Commander, Brigadier General Fitz-John Porter called him in. From his first ascension, Porter had been enthusiastic about ballooning. He manufactured excuses to go aloft with Thad and only the demanding duties of his command kept him on the ground at all.

"I don't have to tell you, Professor, how valuable you are to the army," he told Thad. "But how long do you think you can keep up the killing pace you've been leading? I can't imagine when you sleep!"

In addition to the constant operation of the *Eagle* from dawn till after dark each day, Thad still had to make the arduous journey to Washington every fourth night to replenish the balloon's gas. His only trained assistants were his father and the faithful Captain Dickinson who had joined him while the *Eagle* was being built. These two kept the *Enterprise* in service at the Capital and took care of details for which Thad had neither the time nor the energy.

Wearily Thad told Porter he had been trying for months to provide the army with an organized air reconnaissance team.

"The Department just can't be made to realize that spending money now may mean an incalculable saving in men and material later on."

Porter grunted impatiently. "Submit to me, as soon as possible, a requisition to Ordnance of all your needs. I'll sign it with a strong recommendation for approval, as will General McClellan. It hurts his organizational sense to see this important service run in a hit or miss fashion. He wants it incorporated as a regular corps in the army."

Not wishing to push his luck, Thad asked for only half the equipment he desired: two additional balloons, one with a capacity for 30,000 cubic feet of gas, one for 20,000, with a portable inflating apparatus for each. The cost of the aerostats he estimated at $1500 and $1200 respectively, each gas generator at around $300.

Thad pointed out that inflating the balloons in the field would not only be a great saving in time and trouble, but the hydrogen they produced would render the balloons more buoyant, making higher observations possible.

Included in the requisition were such lesser items as calcium flares for night signaling, colored flags, and powerful telescopes.

On September 16th, General Porter signed the requisition. He had only one criticism:

"You're not asking for enough."

There was one firm condition: the balloons must be manned by aeronauts trained by Professor Lowe.

As the document wended its way from desk to desk, in the maze of officialdom, Thad found his busy days had many pleasant intervals. The activity along the Potomac had attracted interesting "camp followers," among them a group of French noblemen who joined the army during August as observers and aides. Two were childhood friends of Leontine and had shared her flight from France—Philippe, Compte de Paris, son of the "Citizen King" Louis Philippe, and his uncle, the Prince de Joinville.

Innumerable newsmen and artists flocked to the camp. One such "companionable addition" to the corps was Arthur Lumley, an artist from *Leslie's Illustrated Weekly*. He and Matthew Brady, the photographer, availed themselves often of the 1000-foot vantage point Thad's balloon offered.

Thad's work was largely routine spotting. The Rebels had lost the advantage gained at Bull Run, but there remained the nightmare of a lightning attack on Washington. Confederate troops crowded in on Federal fortifications around the Capital's perimeter. Yet McClellan was not ready to push them back.

On September 23rd, Thad was asked to perform an experiment calculated to give the Union troops more elbow room. General W. F. Smith, Battery Commander at a forward post called "Camp Advance" wired General Porter:

> At about 8:30 (8½) tomorrow morning, I wish to fire from here to Falls Church. Will you please send the balloon up from Fort Corcoran, and have note taken of the position reached by the shell, and telegraph each observation at once.

Thad was also to give simple flag signals that General Smith could observe through his glass. He would correct his gunners' fire accordingly.

September 24th, 1861, dawned clear and cool. A ground mist shrouded the sleeping camps as Thad rose above them. The village of Falls Church nestled peacefully amongst green pastures, whose battle scars were concealed by the half-light of early morning.

Thad experienced a moment of horror at what he was about to do. He glanced down at Park Spring, his telegraph operator, who knelt on the floor of the car adjusting his instrument.

"Those men are still asleep over there," Thad said. "They'll never know what hit them."

He had thought of his own role in the war in a detached way, like the working out of a scientific formula. When he considered the human lives involved, it was with the idea of saving, not destroying.

"They're waiting, Professor," Spring reminded him gently.

"Tell them we're ready." According to the prearranged signal Thad waved the white flag to commence firing.

Through his telescope, Thad saw the gunner ram the shot home, ignite the fuse. Then he focused again on Falls Church. It was with relief that he saw the first ball land in an open field to the right of the town.

"At least they're warned," he thought, slowly raising the white flag, indicating that the gunner should correct his range to the left.

The second shot landed on the other side of the village. Thad lowered the flag. The next fell short. He waved it slowly back and forth.

Within minutes after the first blasts civilians and soldiers alike erupted from homes and tents like startled birds. Even the officers, with no seen enemy to attack, seemed momentarily panicked.

As the bombardment continued, Thad reported more and more accurate hits. The Rebels hastily abandoned their positions while Union soldiers marched forward to occupy more advanced posts. Minor skirmishes took place up and down the line.

Confederate batteries on Munson's Hill blasted away at the only thing they could see—the aircraft hovering menacingly in the sky.

As their bullets whistled closer and closer, Thad signalled his crew: "Down!"

On the ground, a message from General Smith awaited Thad.

> The signals from the balloon have enabled my gunners to hit with a fine degree of accuracy an unseen and dispersed target area. This demonstration will revolutionize the art of gunnery.

General Porter personally congratulated Thad. He jumped right into the basket before it was even moored. Looking down he saw that Park Spring was pale and shaken, and his keen eyes noted the reason.

There were two large holes near the floor of the car. A cannon ball had passed directly through between the operator and Thad. Thaddeus had apparently not even noticed it.

"When you're building those new balloons, Professor," said General Porter thoughtfully, "better line your cars with sheet metal!"

That night Thad returned to the Capital to have the balloon inflated and repaired, and to take a well-earned rest. It was almost noon the next day when he was wakened by a knock on his hotel room door. Still groggy from the unaccustomed sleep, he took the note slipped through to him.

Its contents were a dash of cold water for his weary spirits.

> Quartermaster General's Office
> Washington City
> September 25, 1861
>
> On recommendation of Major General McClellan, Secretary of War has directed that 4 additional balloons be at once constructed under your direction, together with

such inflating apparatus as may be necessary. It is desirable that they be completed with the least possible delay.

Very respectfully,
M. C. Meigs.

Thad let out a whoop that might have been heard at the White House!

CHAPTER THIRTEEN

THE CORPS IS BORN

Oil lamps burned day and night in the assembly buildings at Philadelphia as the war balloons were rushed to completion. Supervised by Thad's foreman, Ebenezer Mason, patient artisans snipped and stitched, heedless of the war that thundered ever louder and closer.

Discouragement hung pall-like over Washington that autumn of 1861. The roar of battle echoed in streets and parlors as the Rebels battered the city's defenders. Thad paid small heed, preoccupied as he was with varnish, cordage, and the rising cost of materials.

At the Washington Navy Yard, skilled pipe fitters and shipwrights, ably directed by Henry Forrest, Master Joiner, forged the generators. The incredible square contraptions bore little resemblance to the boiler tubing and cannon which were the usual progeny of the yard's fiery furnaces, its lathes and benches.

Although based on the simple theory of placing iron filings in contact with sulphuric acid, the generators were a maze of tanks and pipes. The unit that contained the running gear had to be strong enough to withstand tremendous pressure while generating gas, yet compact enough to fit an ordinary army wagon.

The design was a tribute to Thad's inventive genius. The yard's fastidious workmen turned out the complicated mechanism for $75 instead of the estimated $300.

Thad's greatest problem was finding willing aeronauts. An independent group, accustomed to taking orders from no one, the men Thad considered serious balloonists could be counted on the fingers of one hand. Half their number had been rivals for the army post.

He had been authorized to offer $3 a day until completion of the aircraft, and he had serious doubts how many could be induced to work for such meager compensation. He wrote to William Paullin, his colleague from Philadelphia, an aeronaut of 28 years' experience; to the Allen brothers, and to John Steiner, a German from Pennsylvania.

He assured each that the corps would be made a regular branch of the army. They would then receive pay "according to the rank designated by the government" and be entitled to pensions and other benefits.

Thad was certain he would receive the rank of Colonel, the others would doubtless be Majors.

"Until the commissions come through," Thad thought, "I can only hope they will consider their patriotic duty above money or rank in other services."

They all accepted his offer and prepared to join him immediately. The Allens even suggested three other balloonists from New England.

While shuttling between Washington and Philadelphia, Thad was still attached to General Porter's division. By October the Army of the Potomac was advancing all along the line, driving the Rebels back towards the Rapidan River.

On October 12th, Thad had just returned from Philadelphia when he received an urgent dispatch from headquarters.

> General McClellan directs that you report to General Smith at Johnson's Hill, be there sure tomorrow, Sunday night.

The armies were engaged near Lewinsville, Virginia. Thad hurriedly summoned his ground crew to inflate the *Eagle* and started off that very evening.

The crew, towing Thad in the balloon, advanced haltingly through Washington and Georgetown, dodging flagpoles, telegraph wires, and trees. High wind made it impossible to elevate the balloon above these hazards. In several places the men had to fell timber to allow the aircraft room to pass.

It was 3 a.m. before they arrived at Chain Bridge. They found it filled with artillery and cavalry. In order to take the balloon over, the men were obliged to walk along the stringers which were only 18 inches wide. Only an occasional flare lit the darkness. A column of artillery moved between Thad's precariously balanced crewmen. The balloon tugged above and the river rushed beneath. At several points, because of bridge supports, the men were obliged to get down off the trestle, then climb back up.

In the balloon car, Thad held his breath, for one false step would catapult them all into the rock-strewn current 100 feet below.

It was daybreak when they reached Lewinsville. The crew was worn out and Thad hoped for a rest period before going into action. After mooring the balloon, he sent some of the soldiers to see what rations were available.

Suddenly the wind, which had abated at sunrise, began to freshen. In a few moments it was a gale.

"Break out the extra-duty ropes," Thad ordered.

The gas envelope of the *Eagle* was tugging against its

netting like a snared monster. A stand of tall trees nearby bent ominously to the howling wind.

Thad and the soldiers were working feverishly to secure the aircraft, when one of the men shouted:

"By gorry! Will you look at that, Perfessor."

Thad glanced up to see an uprooted tree hurtle by. "Come on," he cried, "there's no time to be lost."

The words were hardly spoken when the *Eagle* began to spin like a top. Then men fell back aghast.

"Will you look at them ropes!" gasped one of the men.

The mooring ropes were stretched taut, but it was the balloon netting that drew Thad's attention.

The *Eagle* might have been encased in elastic instead of the strongest hemp. With a succession of reports like the crack of small arms, the netting parted. The gas bag shot up and away, leaving a tangle of rope at the men's feet.

The loss of the *Eagle* left Thad helpless until his new balloons were completed. The generals whom he was to have served pronounced it an unavoidable accident. Thad blamed the vacillation at headquarters causing orders for him to provide proper equipment to be withheld so long.

"This," he wrote Captain Whipple, "the first accident of my life of the kind, prevented me from being of service on this important occasion. . . . With the facilities which will soon be at hand, the accident would not have occurred. Preparations could always be made in a protected spot."

The accident left Thad free to attend to construction details. On October 21st he was ready to make a progress report to Lieutenant Colonel John N. Macomb who had succeeded Captain Whipple as Thad's immediate superior in the Topographical Engineers.

"The balloons are getting along finely," Thad wrote from Philadelphia, "but owing to the uncommonly dull and rainy weather of late the coating does not dry so fast as I would like."

The escaped gas bag had been recovered near Baltimore and delivered to him. After replacing the network and valve, and with fresh varnish, the *Eagle* should be ready for service at the end of the week, he assured Colonel Macomb. There was need for haste since the Confederates were now attempting to blockade the Potomac, cutting off shipping between Washington and Chesapeake Bay.

Several divisions of the Army of the Potomac had been moved down along the river. The first week in November General Joseph Hooker at Budd's Ferry asked for a balloon for mapping and reconnaissance.

The balloon *Constitution* was ready for service, complete with its own generator. William Paullin was to take charge until Thad could train another aeronaut to assist him.

The Commandant at the Navy Yard, Captain Dahlgren, was ready with transportation down river.

"There's your balloon boat," he said proudly. He waved towards an oval flat boat, with mooring hooks in the center and crates at either end for machinery and equipment—"The *George Washington Parke Custis.*"

"It's fine, John," Thad enthused. "Plenty of room to make ascensions, without any funnels or rigging to get fouled in. It should have a shed on the stern to house the generator, though."

"We'll have it fixed up when you're ready to go," Dahlgren promised.

At nightfall of Sunday, November 10th, the carrier's tug, *Coeur de Leon,* nosed her way down the Potomac. She hugged the Maryland bank, to avoid Rebel batteries that lined the Virginia shore. They reached the mouth of Mattawoman Creek before dawn. The unwieldy flatboat had to be towed up the narrow waterway in the dark or risk a barrage from enemy guns.

That evening, when the gear was unloaded and the generator operating, General Hooker ascended with Thad. Confederate campfires on the opposite shore twinkled in the crisp fall evening. They looked almost friendly.

A dawn ascension next day, however, revealed batteries being erected on Freestone Point, three miles away, that looked anything but friendly.

General Hooker remained aloft almost an hour examining army installations and making rough sketches. Thad had to explain a great deal of what he saw.

"Those humps yonder like hills on a relief map, should be counted carefully. They are rows of tents in a pasture, and will give the General an idea how many troops are in the area. The same is true of that low-hanging cloud over towards the horizon. Actually it is dust kicked up by movement on the road."

Thad had learned to distinguish from the looks and size of the cloud how many men were marching, or if it were cavalry, or horses and wagons. He could tell if smoke was from rifle or cannon fire, or just a regiment burning its trash, or cooking supper.

"I hope this man you are leaving with me can distinguish objects from the air as you do," Hooker observed.

"Mr. Paullin is a seasoned aeronaut, but I intend to remain with him a few days to train him in military observation," Thad assured Hooker as he signalled his crew to pull the balloon in.

Suddenly a hum of voices interrupted their conversation. The two men looked down to see a blanket of upturned faces. Excited chatter rose in a wall of sound.

"Why are those men off duty?" exclaimed Hooker angrily. Then unexpectedly he laughed. "Once a showman, always a showman, Professor! Most of those soldiers have never seen a balloon before."

Thad realized that the silk bag with its giant portrait of George Washington must be an imposing sight, floating in the air with no visible means of support.

When he returned to Washington, the Allen brothers were already there. With them were Eben Seaver and J. B. Starkweather, both from Boston. John Steiner joined the group later in the week.

Though competent balloonists, the men had much to learn in a short time—how to handle the new aircraft, military spotting and operation, the running and care of the generators, and how to pack their equipment compactly and quickly.

For each balloon outfit, Thad had also to train 50 enlisted men in inflating, towing, and ascension procedure. The soldiers would serve in a triple capacity as ground crew, maintenance men, and armed guard to protect the detail.

As fast as the balloons and generators were completed, headquarters had an assignment for them. The army's need for air reconnaissance was suddenly so urgent, Thad hardly had time to indoctrinate his assistants. The first call came less than two weeks after the balloonists reported for training.

General Thomas W. Sherman, occuppying Port Royal at the mouth of the Savannah River, South Carolina, requested a balloon detail. On November 27, the *Washington,* its generator, and aeronaut Starkweather were packed aboard the steamer *Mayflower* and sent to that base of operations.

The day after Christmas, a balloon camp was established near Harper's Ferry and Poolesville, at Edward's Ferry. A key spot high in the mountains, it protected Washington on the northwest, where the three states of Virginia, West Virginia, and Maryland meet.

This first air installation was christened Camp Lowe. Eben Seaver was stationed there with the *Intrepid,* one of the larger aircraft.

The Allen brothers kept the *Eagle* operating out of Washington and from the carrier deck on the Potomac. Thad himself remained with Porter's brigade west of the capital. His new balloon, the *Union,* sister ship of the *Intrepid,* still had to be towed back and forth since its generator was not completed.

The aeronautic corps was in full operation and Thad's problems had only begun. Starkweather plagued him with questions ranging in content from wrenches to rations. Eben Seaver found the mountains too cold, his commanding general unappreciative. William Paullin, older than the rest, couldn't take the army rations, the impure drinking water, and the stringent demands of his post. All combined to keep him on the ground more often than in the air.

Thad decided to turn Camp Lowe over to John Steiner and send the younger, less experienced Seaver to assist Paullin at Budd's Ferry. Immediately a tense situation arose between Seaver and Paullin. Seaver became unexpectedly aggressive and demanded absolute authority.

In the course of his investigation, Thad discovered that Paullin was engaging in a little business on the side to augment his meager pay. He had discharged one airman in training only a few days before for gambling. Paullin he merely ordered back to the Capital where his duties would be less arduous.

All the aeronauts asked constantly when they would be commissioned. Yet, in the very short time allowed for organization, the corps was functioning with gratifying efficiency. The Allen brothers proved as quietly competent as Clovis Lowe and Captain Dickinson. While at Camp Lowe, John Steiner was encountering the same problems that had licked Seaver, but with more fortitude.

Snow and hail decomposed the balloon's varnish causing the gas to escape rapidly. Even with a generator on hand, the *Intrepid* was grounded a great deal of the time.

"If you could send me one of the new balloons (two more small aircraft like the *Eagle* were under construction at Philadelphia) and an assistant," the German wrote in his misspelled phonetic English, "I could manage to keep one balloon in operation all the time. Other than that," he continued gamely, "I want nothing but the sun to dry the balloon and net."

Within the week, the *Custis* delivered the *Eagle's* sister craft, the *Excelsior,* at Edwards Ferry. With it came Ebenezer Mason, Thad's young foreman, who had requested active duty.

Less than two weeks later a new demand arose. A flotilla of gunboats under Commodore Foote was attempting to capture islands in the Mississippi. Balloon observations were desired. John Steiner requested the assignment, and left with the *Eagle* for Cairo, Illinois, on February 17th. Ezra Allen replaced him at Camp Lowe.

"You've got to take some time off, son," Clovis told Thad after they packed Steiner off to the west. "Better go home now while everything's running smoothly and the Rebs are dug in for the winter. This may be your last chance to visit your family for a good long while!"

CHAPTER FOURTEEN

THE HAWKS HOVER

Thad and James Allen shivered on a dock in Alexandria as they supervised the loading of the *Intrepid* onto the balloon boat. Flares lit the chill March night. A pungent odor of horse and mule, harnesses, gun powder, and salted meat hung in the damp air.

During the third week of March, a procession of 400 steamers, sailing vessels, craft of every description, had pushed up the Potomac to landing stages at Washington and the little Virginia town across the river.

Night and day, the shouts of teamsters and the staccato commands of a thousand corporals puntuated the constant monotone of pounding hooves and marching feet.

The "magnificent Army of the Potomac" was on the move.

The Confederate forces had withdrawn behind the Rapidan River and braced themselves to defend Richmond against McClellan's formidable army. Out of the demoralized mob of untrained citizens that had deserted the field at Bull Run, the "brilliant young commander" had forged an army of 160,000 troops equipped with every modern device for waging war.

McClellan meant to take the Confederate capital and thus, by one lightning push, end the rebellion. Since the Rebels expected overland pursuit, the army would go by water, down river to Old Point Comfort at the tip of the peninsula formed by the York and the James Rivers. The Grand Army of the Potomac would march on Richmond from the east up the Peninsula.

Thad, James Allen, and Eben Mason were to sail aboard the *George Washington Parke Custis* with the balloon *Intrepid* and two generators. Eben Seaver with his *Constitution* had gone to the Peninsula with Hooker's command earlier in the month. He awaited them at Fortress Monroe, their disembarkation point.

Army wagons and the enlisted detail would follow the balloon boat on transports. The aeronauts' horses and the mules to pull the wagons were packed into holds with 20,000 other animals.

"Those ships will ever after smell like stables," James observed.

"I just hope we can find our own horses at the other end," replied Thad. He was thoughtful, apparently watching a horse being coaxed up a gangplank.

Finally he announced reluctantly: "The Balloon Corps has a new commander for this operation, General A. A. Humphries."

James made no attempt to hide his disappointment. "Still under the Topographical Engineers! And no word about our commissions either, I suppose."

"I write headquarters weekly," Thad told him. "I hate to send men into action without the protection of a uniform. Of course our telegraph operators, all the signalmen, are in the same position. Still . . ."

"Anyway, Humphries is a good man," Thad went on reassuringly. "He'll leave the management of the Balloon Corps to me. That's something!"

By April 2nd, the army had disembarked at Fortress Monroe under cover of Federal gunboats. They spread all across the tip of the Peninsula around Hampton, Virginia.

As Thad watched the columns of armed men cover the plains, he gave a silent salute to the organizational ability of their commander. In two weeks, 125,000 men with all their equipment—McDowell with 40,000 troops had been ordered to remain and guard Washington—some 14,000 horses and mules; 44 batteries; wagons; even pontoon bridges, had been transported 200 miles without the loss of a man or beast!

"Surely such an undertaking is unprecedented in all history!" thought Thad.

On April 3rd, the advance on the Confederate fortress at Yorktown began.

Thad sent his enlisted detail on ahead with the balloons and wagons full of gear to set up camp. General Humphries had assigned Thad a new sergeant. Charles Eaton of the 22nd New York was a regular army man with experience as an Indian fighter.

Thad quickly realized Eaton knew more about marching, camping, and all the problems of an army on the move than he ever would. He was more than happy to turn all details over to him and Wagon Master Robert Collins.

Eben Mason was to remain with Seaver at Fortress Monroe. So Thad and James, having managed to single out their horses from the whinnying herd, rode off alone, a day behind the main bulk of the army.

Incessant rain plagued the expedition. The aeronauts had ridden only a few miles when they ran into baggage trains bogged in heavy mud.

No matter how the drivers cursed and exhorted their mules, the poor beasts could hardly budge the wagons. Many had to be unloaded before they could be extricated. Thad began to watch anxiously for his own men.

The soldiers slogged along wearily, miserable beneath layers of government issue clothing, their heavy boots covered with liquid filth. Thad and James were liberally spattered with the sticky stuff, while their horses were coated with it half way up their bodies.

After leaving Big Bethel, Thad and James began to see overcoats, blankets, even shoes strewn beside the road. The atmosphere was heavy and hot, the rain unrefreshing. The men could hardly be blamed for trying to lighten their loads.

The horses were stumbling with weariness when Thad and James arrived in Yorktown early the next afternoon. Thad went at once to Staff Headquarters, which had been set up in Clarke's farmhouse and Howe's sawmill a mile behind the Union line and two miles from the York River. General Porter, weary and harassed, directed Thad to inflate a balloon immediately.

"I want to go aloft as soon as I can break away," he said.

Thad hurried off to the balloon station situated on a piece of high ground close by. The *Intrepid* took four hours to inflate. There was no time to be lost if an observation was to be made before dark.

At 5 p.m. an officer of Porter's staff appeared. He explained that the General was too occupied to come himself.

The rain has stopped and visibility was excellent as, at 5:20 precisely, the *Intrepid* rose above the Confederate fortifications at Yorktown.

Thad heard the young officer catch his breath.

"You can see right inside the fort," he exclaimed, "—the men's faces—count the guns!" The officer's voice trailed off as his eyes absorbed the panorama spread before him.

Thad imagined the surprise on the upturned faces of the Confederate garrison as they viewed for the first time the new menace. Off-duty soldiers scurried out of the barracks as word apparently spread. Thad laughed as he pointed them out.

"A hawk hovering above a chicken yard could hardly cause more commotion!"

He noted that the opposing armies were entrenched across the Peninsula from Yorktown to Warwick Court House, a distance of about five miles. The next day he was ordered to return to Fortress Monroe and move the *Constitution* to Warwick Court House at the southern end of the Union line.

"Watch out for those Rebel sharpshooters," was his parting advice to James. "They climb trees like monkeys, and when they shoot, they almost never miss!"

The trip back took less than a day as Federal engineers had repaired the railroad, sabotaged by the Rebels. Still Thad was gone for almost a week as he remained with Seaver and Mason till that operation was well under way.

He rode into his own camp at 6 a.m. to find the whole area in turmoil. His appearance seemed to add impetus to the excitement. Everyone tried to talk at once, and gesticulated upwards.

Looking up Thad saw the *Intrepid* sailing majestically over Rebel lines. A tiny figure in the basket appeared to be examining the enemy's installations through the glass.

"That infernal Allen," thought Thad, "he's taken advantage of my absence to try a free flight over enemy territory! I'll teach him to have more respect for government property. We've few enough balloons—or balloonists either for that matter!"

Then a voice below him said:

"I'm sorry, sir. It's all a terrible mistake . . ."

Thad looked down to see his assistant standing beside his horse.

"My word!" exclaimed Thad. "Then who in thunder is up there?"

"It's General Porter, sir. I can explain everything."

"Never mind the explanations," Thad retorted curtly. "We've got to get him down!"

Thad dismounted and ran to his tent. The balloon had descended as the gas dissipated and was wafted back over Union lines. It was directly overhead when Thad emerged from his tent with a megaphone.

"Release the valve," he shouted into the air. "The rope that's painted red."

The end of the valve rope was always painted bright red to distinguish it from the other guide ropes, and it was secured in a separate little compartment. Pulling it by mistake in flight could be disastrous.

Now it seemed the quickest way to get the balloon down.

"Slowly, slowly," Thad cried, when he saw that Porter had found the proper rope. "Take it easy." But it was too late.

In his anxiety to descend, the General had opened the valve wide. The swoosh of escaping gas was clearly audible below. The gas bag collapsed within minutes, but as it did, it folded into the netting, forming a parachute.

The *Intrepid* floated its distinguished passenger right into a shelter tent not 100 rods from General McClellan's headquarters. Then, as if to hide Porter's embarrassment, it collapsed gently, enveloping him in a welter of oil silk, still puffy in spots where gas remained.

Simultaneously a unit of cavalry sent out to follow the balloon's course and pick up the general wherever he might land, rode headlong into camp. Soldiers converged on the scene from all directions. Thad could not get near Porter.

Suddenly he heard a roar. It was the voice of Sergeant Eaton.

"You infernal idiot!" he was bellowing. "Do you want to set fire to the balloon!" Then, "Clear away, all of you!"

The men fell back without a word.

As Thad and James made their way through to Porter, an old tobacco peddler pushed past them. He had a pipe in his mouth, a box of matches still clutched in his hand.

"The old fool must have been lighting his pipe," observed Allen. "He's been skulking about ever since you left. Civilians shouldn't be allowed around camp!"

They found Porter on his back amid silk and tent poles. General Burns stood over him, arm outstretched to give him a hand up.

"I came mounted you see," observed General Porter.

"You're a suspicious character, nevertheless," replied Burns.

"How so?"

"In the space of half an hour you've made off with a balloon, and been arrested by a shelter tent," replied General Burns. The two of them were laughing heartily as the cavalry captain dashed up.

"You are safe, I see," he gasped. "I went with the cavalry to find you."

"You should have sent the flying artillery," retorted Porter, brushing himself off.

Allen's apologies were lost in the general good humor.

"An accident, my boy," General Porter dismissed the whole incident. "My own fault for getting in an untended aircraft. Anyway the view was worthwhile." The general waved a handful of notes and sketches.

"How did such a thing happen?" Thad asked Allen as they retired to their own quarters.

The shamefaced young man explained that he'd gone aloft for the customary dawn reconnaissance then returned for General Porter, who had expressed a desire to make an early ascension. Allen had told the men to moor the balloon with only one rope since he would be using it again immediately. Then he had left to find the general.

"He was not in his quarters so I went right back to the balloon. General Porter was getting in as I approached. A couple of crewmen were holding it." James spread his hands helplessly. "The mooring rope just seemed to pop. The balloon tugged so the men had to let go."

Thad examined the rope in question. "Looks as if some of the acid used in generating got on it and ate through. Weakened it just enough at this spot, see?" He pointed at the frayed ends. "I must warn the men to be more careful."

"Anything else to report?" asked Thad as the two aeronauts sat down to breakfast.

"The enemy is doing everything in its power to destroy the aircraft, but their guns can't reach it," Allen told Thad. "Apparently they've gotten desperate. Their rifle fire is coming from awfully close.

"Yesterday morning," Allen continued, "when I descended to make my report, a small party was sent out to surprise the Rebs in the woods. I was to go aloft again to distract the sharpshooters. While I was still at headquarters, the regular pickets brought in ten prisoners who admitted they were part of a detail sent especially to destroy the aircraft."

James stood up and leaned across the table, as if to emphasize his concern.

"They had been selected for their marksmanship and

given the best rifles, mind you," said James. "They were to get as close to our lines as they could before firing.

" 'The others will get you when you go up again,' one of them said to me. Cocky as you please! There were 35 to begin with, the Reb told us. Most of them were captured or shot before noon."

Sergeant Eaton's gruff voice interrupted. He was standing in the tent entrance.

"I believe they are even trying to infiltrate the camp and sabotage the balloons," Eaton told them. "Take that tobacco peddler. Why, he struck a match, supposedly to light his pipe, when he was right up against the *Intrepid*!"

"You don't think he was just being stupid, Sergeant?" asked Thad.

"Stupid like a fox!" scoffed Eaton.

Within the next few days, two spies were captured as Sergeant Eaton had predicted. The prisoners said they had been offered $1000 in gold and a commission if they destroyed even one balloon. Five had volunteered. No one of them knew who any other was. Each had left the Confederate lines alone. Using whatever disguise he could contrive, each made his separate way into the Federal camp. These two were found working with a gang of Negroes who were building earthworks near the balloon camp.

"How did you spot them?" Thad asked when Eaton pushed the two prisoners into his tent.

"These two fellers was always snoopin' around the balloon." The sergeant laughed. "They was takin' great care not to let the other one see what they was up to, too! I alerted the men to watch 'em every minute.

"When they sweat, the color ran. That was the first tipoff." Eaton ran his finger down the nearest Rebel's cheek to show Thad. "Amateur job. But it was the smell that proved it to me. We used this stuff to disguise like Indians. Smellin' it still makes my stomach churn."

Both spies agreed the old tobacco peddler was probably one of them. He had been run out of camp as a nuisance soon after he lit the match near the balloon.

The army was alerted for attack on the 1st of May. When the Federal artillery began its barrage, the Confederates replied with every conceivable piece of ordnance. Their main target still seemed to be the aircraft. Even the Armstrong guns in their biggest earthwork were trained upward.

The huge parapet of red clay, known as the "Red Fort," was part of fortifications built by the British under Cornwallis, and remodeled by the Confederates. It had become a familiar landmark to Thad.

Shot after shot from its cannon whistled close around the balloon, destroying trees and gouging huge holes in the earth below. General Porter stood calmly beside Thad in the basket, knowing as well as the aeronaut that they were out of range.

"Odd, the sudden concentration of fire," Porter remarked. "Something's afoot. Better keep a close watch."

Below, the men were not so cool.

"Why don't he come down?" cried one. "That last shell came pretty close."

"If the balloon is hit, that's the end of Lowe," another said shaking his head.

Cavalry General Stoneham was concerned, but not for Thad's safety. He became more furious with each shell percussion. Finally he stomped over to McClellan's headquarters.

"I've got my horses to think of," he told the commander. "They hump up their backs every time those siege guns are fired. They'll all be nervous wrecks before we ever go into battle. You'll have to have that balloon camp moved."

As the generals stood talking, a shell destroyed a nearby tent.

"I'll have Lowe move camp immediately he comes down, General," McClellan assured his cavalry leader, brushing the dirt from his uniform.

In the balloon above their heads, Thad and James were watching one gun crew in the "Red Fort."

"If they try to roll that cannon any higher, it'll explode," Allen observed.

"They should know by now we're out of range of any gun they've got," replied Thad. As he spoke, he saw one of the gunners spark the fuse.

Suddenly the fort was enveloped in smoke and flame as the big gun burst. Amid flying debris, Thad saw dismembered parts of the gunners who had become as familiar to him as old friends. He felt himself retch.

"Better give the signal to pull us down," he told his assistant. When there was no reply he turned to find James clutching the edge of the basket, his face stark white, eyes staring.

Thad gave the signal himself.

That evening the balloon camp was moved to another area, near General Heintzelman's quarters. Thad was sitting with the elderly officer enjoying the soft spring night when a 12-inch shell was lobbed into the telegraph tent nearby. Fortunately it did not explode, but the general and the aeronaut were covered with what seemed tons of dirt, and much of the valuable equipment was destroyed.

"Looks like they've already found our new location," said Thad, trying to brush the dirt off Heintzelman's uniform. "I guess I'll have to move again."

The old general laughed. "I can stand it if you can. Like to have you near me. I want to go aloft early in the morning. I have a feeling those Rebs are getting ready to pull out on the sly. The Confederate stand here could only have been a delaying action at best."

At midnight Thad was wakened by Captain Moses, Heintzelman's aide. "There's a big fire over towards Yorktown. The General wishes you to go aloft and see what it is."

Thad rose into a dark night sky, but Yorktown was brightly lit by a fire near the docks. From the location of the blaze, he knew it to be a supply depot that was burning. He concluded the fire was an accident, incidental to what was actually occurring.

The fortress and surrounding earthworks were alive with an activity that would be surprising even at midday.

Thad descended and told Captain Moses to fetch General Heintzelman at once. Aloft once more, Thad drew Heintzelman's attention to the steady stream of wagons going in and out of the fort.

"I believe you were correct, sir. They're pulling out!"

The blaze had died down and the line of wagons was only dimly discernible. General Heintzelman squinted through the glass for a better look, then shook his head.

"There are more wagons going in than out. I believe they're replenishing their supplies."

"Excuse me, sir," Thad interjected. "Watch the wagon wheels in the light of those camp fires beside the road."

Heintzelman studied the wagons through the telescope for several minutes.

"I can see more wheel on those going in." The officer was frankly puzzled.

"That is because the ones coming out are the ones that

are loaded," Thad explained. "You can only see the bottom half of the wheels."

The general watched seconds more, then clapped Thad on the back. "By jiminy, Professor, you're right. They're trying to steal the march. Let's get down. We'll catch them before they've gone five miles!"

By dawn the whole Union line was alerted and preparing to march. The muted rattle of 10,000 bridles and the rasp of sabers being drawn broke the still dawn. Stoneman's cavalry was preparing to make the first dash.

Thad brought word to McClellan that as far as eye could see there was not a single camp in or around Yorktown, nor in the whole Confederate defense line. The fortifications seemed completely deserted.

The men of the signal corps moved forward, repairing telegraph wires as they went, and searching for hidden explosive charges. From aloft Thad watched admiringly as the signalmen righted poles and restrung wires with amazing speed. He saw the familiar figure of Chief Telegraphist D. D. Lathrop descending a pole close to the Confederate fort. For some reason, he wanted to cry out to the man. Then he saw Lathrop's feet touch the ground, and instantly man and pole were enveloped in smoke and dirt.

"Oh, my God. . . !" Thad turned away, shaken and sick.

Lathrop had stepped on the primer of a buried torpedo. He was killed instantly, the only casualty entering Yorktown.

At that moment the sound of bugles rose in the air. The cavalry and the horse artillery swept across the battered Confederate breastworks, sabers flashing, flags whipping.

CHAPTER FIFTEEN

THE CARRIER LEADS

Not a church bell rang in the village of Yorktown that Sunday, May 4th, 1862. As Thad's crew towed him forward in the *Intrepid,* he saw no sign of life in the Rebel fortress and earthworks, but he remained alert for sharpshooters on the river bluffs and in the woods. The Union horsemen had already disappeared into the rainsoaked forests.

"Let's go up on the Red Fort and see the damage," Thad called to his crew.

The cannon that had destroyed itself trying to shoot the *Intrepid* out of the sky lay on its side. Ammunition boxes and powder kegs were scattered about. Sand seeped from the punctured sides of the bags that had protected the gunners. The ram used to drive the shot home lay where it had been dropped by its handler.

Remembering the determined young faces of the Confederate gun crew, Thad touched the cold iron of the big gun and sighed.

"Let's go!" He summoned his men who were nosing around curiously, picking up souvenirs.

Aloft again, he turned his glass towards the York River. Gloucester Point, a high jut of land on the north bank opposite Yorktown, had been cleared of enemy batteries by the seven Federal gunboats that waited now beneath the cliff, ready to move upstream. Several miles east, at the mouth of the York, Thad saw a strange flat boat and several transports just entering the river from Chesapeake Bay.

"That couldn't be the *Monitor,*" Thad thought as he studied the low craft intently. "She should still be outside Hampton Roads watching for the *Merrimac* . . . unless she's destroyed the Confederate ironclad."

Thad watched the approaching fleet for several minutes. Then he burst into a roar of laughter that caused the crew to look up, startled.

"Here comes our balloon boat," he shouted, "sailing up the river with the troop transports. I mistook it for the *Monitor*!"

The sound of the men's laughter rang happily in the silence.

Thad's father was aboard the carrier with the *Washington.* Aeronaut Starkweather had brought the balloon back to Washington after Union forces occupied Fort Pulaski, closing the Savannah River to southern blockade runners.

"Jeb had his fill of war," Clovis reported. "I left him to operate the *Excelsior* outside the Capital."

Thad shook his head. "We could have used him here. Seaver had to go home April 30th. His family were about to be evicted from their home. None of us have received our pay since leaving Washington. This campaign is apt to be rugged, but I guess you'd better stay with us, Dad."

Clovis looked pleased. "I'm not too old for a good fight yet, son."

Eben Mason and his detail arrived from Warwick Courthouse just after noon. All three aircraft, their generators and crews, went aboard the carrier and its tug. They were to sail with the transports and gunboats up the York to West Point, thence up the Pamunkey to White House Landing, McClellan's new base of supplies. Balloons would be useless in the center of the Peninsula around Williamsburg because of the heavy forests.

By mid-afternoon, the carrier was ready to sail. The transports were still loading the army division that was to guard the new supply base, their baggage and food, as well as the cannon and mortars, and tons of ammunition that had never been needed to take Yorktown.

"We might as well start," Thad decided. "We can keep someone aloft to watch for the enemy. Doubtless the others will sail by evening."

The banks of the river were lined with cotton-bale fortifications but they were deserted. At sundown the carrier reached West Point, at the mouth of the Pamunkey.

The following morning Thad ascended at dawn. Mist over the river prevented a clear view. Inland he glimpsed isolated bands of retreating Confederate soldiers, but there was no sign of his own army. Constant rain had made the roads almost impassable which doubtless accounted for the delay. He decided to continue up the winding Pamunkey, keeping an aeronaut aloft to watch for an ambush.

They arrived at White House Landing at 6 p.m. The Richmond and York River Railroad bridge, which crossed the Pamunkey at that point, had been fired and was still burning.

Only then did Thad realize the precariousness of their position. The little balloon guard, 150 men with muskets, not counting the aeronauts, constituted the advance picket of the Army of the Potomac.

Thad was mulling over their situation when Sergeant Eaton approached him.

"Excuse me, sir," Eaton said. "I spied scouts along that ridge yonder through your glass. There's no movement as if they was comin' after us. But when they make sure we're alone . . ."

His words were an uneasy sequel to Thad's own thoughts.

"With your permission, Professor," the sergeant continued, "I'd like to have the men set up their tents amongst the trees there on the river bank . . . far apart, so they'll reach way down the river. Them Rebs will see all our tents. But strung out like that, they may think there's more in the woods."

"We hope. . . !" Thad interjected.

"To make sure, I'd build as many campfires as the men can gather material to make," Eaton went on.

"An old Indian trick, eh, sergeant?" Thad laughed. "Well, it may work, so long as those scouts weren't Indian fighters too. Go ahead. Just leave me a few men. I'm going up to the house."

The White House loomed majestically above them, on a bluff that commanded a wide sweep of country up and down the river. It was the home of William H. F. Lee, son of Robert E. Lee. George and Martha Washington had resided in it for a time, and named their official residence at Washington for the stately mansion.

When Thad entered the manor house, he felt its emptiness was not that of a house long unoccupied. There were indications everywhere of a family in residence: knitting dropped hurriedly on a table; the ball of worsted rolled across the drawing room floor, spectacles lying on an open book.

The dining room confirmed his suspicion. The evening meal had just been placed on the table. The covered dishes steamed when he lifted their lids, and the tea in the pot was still warm.

Thad deployed his men to search the grounds. They found the overseer and two house servants who only grunted sullenly when questioned. Thad marched them back to camp, hoping for better luck later.

The dawn reconnaissance next day revealed that the Rebel scouts on the ridge two miles away had made no move towards the tiny Federal force.

"Maybe they think the carrier is the *Monitor,* too," Clovis remarked.

At 8 a.m. Thad spotted a column of horsemen approaching, up the Peninsula. He watched them for several moments through his glass; finally satisfied himself it was Union cavalry.

Within the hour, General Stoneman strode up to the White House where Thad awaited him on the porch.

"This is a surprise," he exclaimed, grasping Thad's hand. "I thought I was in the lead towards Richmond. I see I was mistaken."

Obviously pleased to find the aeronaut and his corps, Stoneman seemed to have forgotten the incident of the frightened horses at Yorktown.

"And I don't need to tell you how relieved we are to see you, sir," Thad told Stoneman. "What kept you so long?"

General Stoneman sank wearily into a porch chair.

"We caught up with the Rebs six miles out of Yorktown and skirmished with Jeb Stuart's cavalry who were protecting their rear. Meanwhile the Army occupied the fortifications at Williamsburg. We fought all of yesterday."

Stoneman made a wry face. "The dead and wounded were half buried in mud. We could hardly move. The artillery and the horses couldn't charge, the stuff was so heavy." He shrugged his shoulders. "And, after all, the devils got away!"

During the next few days, the Army of the Potomac straggled in to White House Landing, muddy and weary. General McClellan set up temporary headquarters on the lawn of the Lee mansion, but never would set foot in the "traitor's" house.

On May 17th, the army began its march south towards Richmond. The aeronauts and their wagons rode with the cavalry. Once again the balloon corps spearheaded the approach to Richmond, but this time they were well protected.

Thad and General Stoneman had their first view of the southern capital and its encircling breastworks on May 20, from a height north of the Chickahominy River called Gaines Hill. Though barely five miles from their goal, the river between was flooded and every bridge destroyed by the retreating Confederates.

"This is an excellent spot for my main camp," Thad told Stoneman, who had chosen a nearby bluff for the artillery. He asked Thad to see if the plantation's owner was still in residence.

Thad rode with an orderly across a field of wheat that extended on either side for at least 1000 acres. Before him was an imposing array of buildings described on the General's map as "Dr. Gaines' Farm." As their horses jumped the fence and approached the house, they were confronted by an imposing gentleman. He looked furious.

"Gentlemen!" he cried. "Why could you not have taken the road to reach the house instead of riding through and tramping down so fine a field of grain?"

Thad dismounted and approached the man. Having ascertained it was Dr. Gaines whom he addressed, he apologized.

"But," he told the doctor, "our army is just behind me and will soon occupy its most commanding position which, unfortunately, is where we are standing."

Doctor Gaines paled as he saw Federal soldiers approaching across the field. Thad told the orderly to place a guard around the house and gardens. The artillery occupied the bluff on either side.

Thad had his tents pitched in a locust grove near the house. That evening, as the aeronauts sat down to supper, a servant from the house appeared with a tray of garden luxuries, fresh tomatoes, kale, and black-eyed peas, delicacies the men had not enjoyed for weeks.

"The doctah wishes to thank you for protectin' his home and family, suh," the servant announced.

Rummaging through his meager stores, Thad picked out several jars of preserves. Placing them on the tray, he told the servant to return his compliments to the doctor and his family.

During the next five days the Army of the Potomac spread out along the north bank of the Chickahominy River, which flowed through the center of the peninsula, passing four miles north of Richmond at Mechanicsville. The men went to work immediately to rebuild the bridges.

Just below Thad's headquarters, the men working on a rough log bridge were constantly harassed by enemy troops hidden among the trees on the opposite banks. The artillery on Gaines' Hill could fire all day, never finding a target.

On May 25th, General Stoneman ascended with Thad to seek out the hidden Rebels. Accurate fire directed from the 1000-foot vantage point caused them to retreat. The general then trained the glass up river on the town of Mechanicsville, still held by the Confederates.

The Federal troops must take the town and sever the steel jugular of the Virginia Central Railroad tracks, one of Richmond's major supply lines.

"If they can use the woods for cover, so can we," Stoneman told Thad. "You go aloft at 3 a.m. to draw their attention. I'm going to borrow a brigade of infantry and give the Rebs at Mechanicsville a surprise party."

CHAPTER SIXTEEN

AN ARMY SAVED

The evening of May 26th, a scout stole out from Richmond bringing several copies of that city's newspaper. Thad was amused to find he was famous there. He read:

> The enemy are fast making their appearance on the banks of the Chickahominy. Yesterday there was a balloon in the air all day. They evidently discovered something of importance for at 4 a.m. this morning brisk cannonading was heard at Mechanicsville and the Yankees now occupy that place.

The paper said that Richmond citizens watched the Federal balloons from their housetops. It even described the ornamentation on the gas envelope which could be discerned through telescopes.

From the base at Mechanicsville, only four miles from the Confederate capital, the aeronauts felt like "Peeping Toms." Through the telescope they could "look into the windows of Richmond," and watch the people scurrying about in the streets.

During May, Federal troops had occupied Norfolk, at the mouth of the James River. The Confederate ironclad *Merrimac,* or the *Virginia* as they had named it, had been scuttled. General McClellan was anxious to move his base to the James, since there was now nothing to prevent the Union Navy from sailing up the river to aid in the siege of Richmond.

Several corps under General Heintzelman had crossed the Chickahominy when word from Washington caused a delay. McClellan was advised that McDowell, with his army of 40,000 troops that had remained to protect the capital, was marching down the Shenandoah Valley to join him. The commander had no choice but to wait for the reinforcements although it left his army dangerously divided by the flooded Chickahominy.

The day after Mechanicsville was taken, Thad stationed the balloon *Washington* there, with James Allen in command. Mason had gone home sick, so Clovis was Thad's only other assistant. Thad rode the six miles from his main camp at Gaines' Hill twice a day to help Allen and check his reports.

Confederate troops on the south bank of the Chickahominy opposite Mechanicsville were being increased. McClellan became convinced the Rebels planned to retake the town and then thrust northward to cut his supply line from the Pamunkey.

On May 29th, Thad noted unusual enemy activity just opposite his "eagle's nest" on Gaines' Hill. The Rebels were trying to hide their operations in the trees.

"I have a feeling," he told General McClellan, "they may attack Heintzelman's isolated force."

On the strength of this report, a few reserves were sent across a flooded footbridge to bolster Federal positions on the south bank.

Just before noon on May 31st, Thad was aloft at Mechanicsville when he saw troops and wagon trains streaming out of Richmond. They were moving east towards Seven Pines and Fair Oaks Station, the center of Heintzelman's first line of defense, across the river from Thad's main camp. At the same time, he noted that the Rebel brigades opposite Mechanicsville were marching south and east to converge with their comrades.

Now Thad was certain they planned to attack the small Union force across the river. He shouted to Allen through his megaphone to dispatch a messenger to Gaines' Hill with orders to inflate the *Intrepid* at once. He needed the larger balloon to carry the additional weight of telegraph equipment and operator high enough to observe the whole battlefield.

Before descending, Thad swept his telescope downstream, where men were still trying to repair the bridges. Torrential rains the night before had destroyed much of the new, but rude construction. The main body of the Army of the Potomac was separated from Heintzelman's threatened position by an impassable expanse of water!

Thad took one last look at the gray-clad horde across the river, advancing ruthlessly. . . .

He galloped the six miles to Gaines' Hill to find the *Intrepid* only partially inflated. Impatiently he leaped into the smaller *Constitution*.

A quick observation showed the two Confederate forces had met and were taking up battle formation. He estimated that they comprised better than three divisions.

The Federal troops, with barely one division, were bracing themselves to meet the onslaught. General Heintzelman was riding up and down the lines giving orders and encouragement. Every once in awhile, he seemed to look upwards toward the balloon. Thad pictured the cherubic face, distorted with desperation lest his men be annihilated before help could reach them.

Thad gave the signal to be pulled down. Without hesitation he wrote the most important dispatch of his career, calculated to alter McClellan's strategy.

Brigadier-General March
Chief of Staff

There are large bodies of troops in the open field beyond the opposite heights on the New Bridge Road. White-covered wagons are rapidly moving towards the point of the engagement with artillery in advance.

T. S. C. Lowe
Chief Aeronaut

Then Thad turned his attention to the problem of getting the *Intrepid* into the air. Normally it would take another hour to inflate her—a precious hour during which constantly telegraphed reports of enemy movements might spell the difference between victory and defeat.

Suddenly Thad's eye was caught by a 10-inch camp kettle hanging in front of the galley tent.

"Get that kettle and cut the bottom out of it," he ordered. "Quick! There's no time to lose," he urged.

"Now," he told the crew holding the *Constitution,* "bring her right next to *Intrepid.*" Then as the de-bottomed kettle was brought him, "Pull the *Intrepid* off the generator and connect her intake valve to the kettle's spout."

Meanwhile he placed the open bottom of the kettle over the *Constitution*'s valve. "Now release her valve." A connection had been made and within a quarter of an hour the gas from the smaller balloon had completed the inflation of the larger. An hour at least had been gained!

Staff officers later estimated that hour saved the Federal government $1,000,000 a minute.

Chief Telegraphist, Park Spring, who had rejoined Thad after Lathrop's death, was already in the *Intrepid*'s car with his equipment. They ascended immediately.

The opposing forces across the river were fully engaged.

Cannon smoke and thick groves of trees made it difficult to see, but the Union line seemed to be holding.

"Heintzelman is nobly sustaining himself against great odds in favor of the enemy," Thad dictated to Spring.

Directly below Thad, two divisions of General Sumner's corps, in full battle dress, awaited orders to cross the swollen river. The log bridge was afloat, prevented from drifting downstream by tree stumps and ropes attached to felled trees. It seemed impossible for the soldiers to cross it.

The water continued to rise. The attempt must be made soon—or never.

It was nearly four o'clock before Thad saw an orderly dash up to General Sumner.

"It's got to be orders to cross!" thought Thad.

A shout went up as one brigade after another swarmed over the swaying bridge. The men's weight pressed it down between the tree stumps, and it held firm.

Once across, the troops hurried on, guided by the roar of the battle that could be heard for miles.

The artillery was left behind in the swamp. The horses floundered in the mud. The cannoneers, pulling at the beasts' bridles, or pushing, shoulders to the cannons' heavy wheels, sank almost to their waists.

During a lull, Thad saw that the Union columns across the river had broken and fallen back to their second line of defense. Relief had come none too soon.

The fresh troops stiffened the line. Thad saw them charge and charge again, finally driving the Confederates back.

That evening Thad was visited by the French observers, who had watched the battle from McClellan's headquarters. The first major engagement between the Confederate Army of Northern Virginia and the Grand Army of the Potomac had left them impressed and excited.

The Prince de Joinville confided to Thad: "Most of the high command thought the attack on the right bank might be a feint to draw Federal troops while the main body of Confederates debouched on the left. But the vehemence of the attack as reported by you put an end to their doubt. It was then Sumner's divisions were ordered to cross the river. You, sir, saved the day!"

"Do they expect a fresh attack tomorrow?" Thad asked.

"Oh, I think not," the Prince replied. "They feel the Rebels will run right back to Richmond."

Thad was not convinced the emergency was over. He decided to make an ascension before retiring. The lights that twinkled amongst the trees on the opposite shore seemed too numerous to be just diligent seekers of the wounded.

In the air again at daybreak the following morning, he confirmed his suspicion that the Confederate Army had never left the field. And every road out of Richmond was filled with reinforcing infantry and cavalry.

Thad's early report gave the Federals time to entrench.

"They must have sent every available soldier against us," he pointed out to Spring. "The big barracks to the left of Richmond is entirely free of smoke. In fact the whole city is. I can see the earthworks around it clearly."

The battle raged throughout the day while the *Intrepid* and the *Washington* at Mechanicsville remained aloft, sending reports to headquarters at fifteen-minute intervals —reports that buzzed over the wires to the War Department in Washington.

President Lincoln himself heard, almost as it happened, the story of that dreadful day beside the Chickahominy.

By evening, every forest lane and swampy field was strewn with the dead and dying. Blue- and gray-clad figures lay within a few feet of each other.

At 6:30, Thad reported:

> Last firing is two (2) miles nearer Richmond than this morning. Campfires around Richmond as usual—showing that the enemy is back.

And at 7 p.m.

> Enemy still in field opposite here and works visible all along the Williamsburg and New Bridge Roads to Richmond. Barracks this morning deserted now occupied. Can see no wagons moving in any direction.

CHAPTER SEVENTEEN

ON TO RICHMOND!

Confederate leaders knew as well as Union officers the important role the balloons had played in turning their attack at Fair Oaks.

After the battle, the Rebels held their position across the river from Thad's main camp at Gaines' Hill. Every time Thad made an ascension, he was greeted with a hail of shot and shell. Every piece of ordnance the enemy had seemed to be turned on him.

One morning a Yankee reporter, George Alfred Townsend, was aloft with Lowe over Mechanicsville. It was a brilliant day. The people on the streets of Richmond, even the shining waters of the James River, alive with gunboats and transports, were clearly visible.

Townsend had just started making notes when he heard his companion exclaim. A dozen shots whistled through the balloon's rigging. A resounding "ping, ping" told the men that several shot had hit the sheet metal that lined the basket.

"They've got us foul, this time!" said Thad. Then he leaned over the edge of the car and shouted to the crew, "Haul in the cables. Quick!"

"Another shot will do our business," he told the newsman. "They've pulled twelve of their largest cannon right down in the swamp across the river." He pointed as he spoke. "It isn't a mile and they've got our range!"

Just then the men felt another whizzing shock, so close that pieces of shell were driven across their faces. They were knocked to the floor of the car. Townsend closed his eyes and held his breath.

After endless seconds, the reporter opened his eyes. Thad was on his feet clutching the cordage.

"Are you pulling in there, men!" he was bellowing.

Townsend struggled to his feet. He saw, below, men running from all directions, signal flags waving. Across the river, gunners in gray were methodically swabbing their cannon, ramming the shot home, again aiming at the helpless aircraft.

He saw the cannon puff—heard a splutter and crash.

"My God!" Thad cried. "They've opened from another battery!"

Townsend felt cold dew break out all over him. The aeronaut and his voice wavered and dissolved. . . .

He was next aware of an excited voice—"Pitch water on his face!"

Townsend winced, waiting for the dousing.

"He ain't used to it." Another voice penetrated his consciousness.

"Hello," said the first voice, "he's coming to."

Townsend had to force his eyes open. Curious, solicitous faces hovered over him. He turned his head to see the balloon, lying on its side nearby. He himself lay prone on the blessed earth.

The reporter reached both hands out, palm down, to feel the solid ground.

A roar went up from the men. Thad lifted Townsend to his feet.

"Three cheers for the Union balloon," cried the men. Townsend added his feeble voice to the cheer.

"Hip, hip, hoorooar!"

When McClellan heard about the incident he ordered both balloon camps moved back from the river. All unauthorized persons were forbidden to go aloft.

Among those Lowe had to refuse was a visitor from Germany, Count Ferdinand von Zeppelin. The young nobleman haunted the balloon camp. His fascination with the aircraft struck a chord of sympathy in Thad.

He finally arranged for Zeppelin to go to Poolesville. "One of my best men is there with the *Union,* sister ship of the *Intrepid,*" he told the German lad. "He will be honored to take you up, and can explain everything in your native tongue, which he speaks better than English."

Thad felt an unaccountable disappointment when the youth left.

"For some reason, I feel cheated that I could not give Count Zeppelin his first balloon ride," he told Clovis.

Regular army officers from other countries who were military observers became volunteer aides with McClellan's staff so they could participate in all operations.

Captain Beaumont of Her Britannic Majesty's government, was a frequent passenger in the balloons. He took voluminous notes with the avowed intention of creating an identical air arm for the British Army.

He always called the aeronaut "General" despite his civilian clothes.

"He must be a Brigadier, at least," Beaumont would insist. "Lowe is a clever man, indefatigable in carrying out his work in the face of gravest danger. He must be one of the highest paid men in the Union Army!"

During those early June days, Thad watched helplessly as column after column of reinforcements entered Richmond from the south and west. Why had McClellan delayed so long!

In the swamps below, another enemy attacked the Federal troops. The bottomlands were infested with malaria, the waters rank. Two thousand soldiers were invalided home. Many more, attacked intermittently by fever and chills, carried on.

Thad's own sergeant, Charles Eaton, died a victim of typhoid fever.

On June 25th, Thad spied large bodies of troops moving down the Shenandoah Valley, into Ashland, seventeen miles from Richmond. At that distance it was impossible to tell if the troops wore blue or gray, especially as they seemed to waver and shimmer before his eyes in a very odd way.

"Must be heat waves," Thad told himself, then shivered as if in contradiction. He decided to take a staff officer up with him. "Maybe it's McDowell at last, come to reenforce our attack," was his wishful thought.

But when General Porter went aloft he confirmed Thad's worst fear. As the dust cloud had indicated, a whole army was approaching. But it was the Confederate army, commanded by "Stonewall" Jackson, against which McDowell was still defending Washington! The Rebel fox had sneaked from under the Union general's nose, leaving only a token force to fool him.

June 26th dawned bright and clear, promising a brilliant summer day, hot and dry. Thad wondered what trick of fate had withheld the fine weather until the pendulum had swung in favor of the Rebels.

From above Mechanicsville, he could just glimpse bits of the Confederate forces massed across Meadow Bridge, cleverly concealed by the natural formation of the ground so he could not tell their number. Only Federal outposts remained at Mechanicsville. Porter had withdrawn to make a stand at Beaver Dam Creek, a naturally strong position, two miles east of Mechanicsville.

Thad turned his glass to examine the vast clouds of dust to the north and west, indicating the approach of Jackson's force. He was still far away, and Porter had arranged to delay him at least that day.

That was the last reconnaissance from Mechanicsville. Thad left Allen to direct the packing of the *Washington,* its generator and other gear, while he returned to Gaines' House. Allen joined him there later in the morning.

At noon, a single cannon fired at Mechanicsville signaled the advance of the Rebel forces across the Chickahominy. Lowe could see them swarming across the Mechanicsville and Meadow Bridge. According to plan, the Federals offered little resistance as they fell back behind Beaver Dam Creek, destroying bridges.

The Confederates marched down the north bank of the Chickahominy as if on parade. They must have known they would be stopped, but they walked right into the Beaver Dam Valley and a withering wall of fire from Federal artillery left wounded and dead strewn all over the hillside and road.

The aeronaut had not stayed to see the slaughter. He heard the screams of dying men as his crew pulled him down.

"There's nothing to be done up there," he explained, as he hurried away, white-faced and shaken. Thad just made the shelter of some trees when he became violently ill.

The battle was over at sundown but anguished cries

haunted his feverish dreams. Occasionally the night was rent by a sound he had come to know and hate, the unearthly scream of a wounded horse.

He started up several times to consciousness of activity in the camp around him. But with no will to discover why the soldiers were not resting, he fell again into troubled sleep.

It was nearly dawn when his father shook him awake. "They're moving the siege guns to the south bank!" Clovis' voice was urgent. "We're to take the balloons and all our equipment across at once. The army is retiring to Powhite Swamp, just below here by the Lower Trestle Bridge."

"But why?" Thad protested. "We stopped Longstreet's men, didn't we? Why are we retreating?"

"General McClellan came over to confer with General Porter during the night," Clovis told him. "Apparently they expect General Jackson to join Longstreet today. Something delayed him yesterday or we might not have held. He'll attack from the north, endangering our right. Porter is to pull his forces into a tighter formation at the new line, and protect the bridges below for a strategic withdrawal across the Chickahominy."

Thad drew a hand across his damp forehead. His eyes stung and his head felt like an overripe melon. He found it difficult to follow his father's words.

"Doubtless General McClellan will advance on Richmond while we keep the Confederate armies busy here." Thad looked at his father for confirmation of the hope. The familiar face blurred.

He felt his father's hand on his forehead. It was like ice.

"You feel like you've got fever, Thaddeus." Clovis stepped out of the tent and returned in a moment with a damp handkerchief. Thad wiped his face and the coolness helped to clear his foggy mind. He jumped to his feet.

"Tell the men to take the *Intrepid* across the river," he instructed his father. "She's inflated and ready to go. You and James follow as soon as possible with the other balloons and the generators. Try not to abandon any equipment."

"You can't go up, Thaddeus," Clovis protested. "You're sick!"

But his son was gone.

At 8:15 Thad and Park Spring were in the air, looking back across the Chickahominy towards the old headquarters. There was heavy cannonading in the area east of Dr. Gaines' house. Thad turned his glass towards Richmond. The whole countryside was so covered with smoke he could see nothing.

"Send a dispatch to headquarters," he told Spring. "Say that I am very unwell and think it advisable for a good person to be up constantly."

Word came back that Clovis and Allen were still desperately trying to save the equipment. Thad learned later that his ground crews, wagons, and horses had been appropriated for other duties. His assistants had had to get the balloon property to safety, aided only by Spring's assistant, Charles Fonda.

At 9:20 Thad reassured headquarters he would remain in the air as long as necessary and requested two orderlies to carry dispatches in case wire communications were cut. He added:

> North from here two and a half 2½ miles from river, large bodies of troops in open field—too far to right to be the enemy. Long line of skirmishers on hill to side of Gaines House. Field nearby on fire.

Thad swept his glass west and south again.

"I must be delirious," he remarked to his telegraphist. "Look yonder."

Spring rose from his crouched position over the telegraph key and peered over the edge of the basket.

"If you're delirious so am I, Professor, because I see it too."

They saw another balloon floating about 300 feet in the air, four miles west of them, in front of Richmond. What made the two men doubt their senses were its many garish colors that glinted and shimmered in the bright June sun. It looked as if Joseph's "coat of many colors" of biblical fame had been inflated and sent aloft.

For several minutes Thad and his telegrapher stared at the gay, multihued bauble, incongruous in this grim setting. Then they turned their attention back to the business at hand.

At 2 p.m. the Rebels hurled a vicious attack against the Union lines. Wave after wave of gray-clad infantry dashed across the plains, floundering in swamp and underbrush. Whole brigades seemed to melt away before withering fire from Federal artillery and small arms, only to be replaced by fresh regiments.

The roar and crash of the battle was deafening even at Thad's remote observation post. As the afternoon wore on smoke mercifully shrouded the spectacle. The Union lines held firm and at four Thad noted with relief Federal troops crossing Woodbury's Bridge to relieve Porter's men who had been engaged unceasingly for two days.

The enemy on Gaines' Hill made one last desperate advance on Porter's right in an effort to outflank the Federals and intercept the crossing at Woodbury's Bridge. Thad saw the enemy repulsed and strong guards placed at every crossing of Powhite Creek. By six o'clock the battlefield was still.

"I guess they've finished killing one another for today," Thad said dispiritedly. "Even the Rebs' bright balloon is gone." He signaled the men below to pull them down.

When the ill balloonist's feet touched ground, the fever he had ignored all day consumed him. In the delirium that followed he comprehended nothing.

Later he learned that the silence across the river had been ominous rather than peaceful, had lasted only half an hour. Then the Rebels had descended on Porter's weary battalions, now almost without ammunition, and with guns so foul from continued use that they could not be loaded rapidly enough to meet the onrushing horde.

That night, under cover of darkness, what was left of Porter's men, still undefeated, retired across the Chickahominy, burning the bridges behind them.

On the morning of June 28th, the balloon corps was ordered to Harrison's Landing on the James.

Thad was spared the "strategic withdrawal" across the marshes and plains to the James. For five days McClellan's army, still not admitting defeat, marched by night and fought by day. He missed their valiant stand at Malvern Hill.

Thad lay amongst the wounded at Malvern House, and their groans and cries mingled and blended with his delirious dreams. Sometimes he thought he heard the cannon roar and saw the limbs of blasted men blown high as his balloon.

He saw the sun glint on a general's saber. He saw it rise and fall and heard the cry: "Forward" and: "March." The cry grew louder and louder until it was a piercing scream that echoed: "On to Richmond!"

Thad sat up on his straw palette wild-eyed—suddenly and horribly awake—knew it was he who had screamed—and knew it was too late.

CHAPTER EIGHTEEN

HOME

"We're goin' to give your Uncle Thad the biggest fish dinner he ever had!" Charles Edward told his son Vyron. "Get the boys together and we'll go up the ravine fishin'."

Thad and his family had been in Jefferson, New Hampshire all summer. He had left the army in May, 1863, finally thwarted by the rigidity of official minds, sick in heart and body from prolonged exhaustion and the malarial fever, legacy of the Chickahominy swamps.

When the Grand Army of the Potomac was recalled from the Peninsula in August, 1862, the Aeronautic Department existed in name only. Clovis had kept the balloons in order, the faithful Allens and Captain Dickinson stood by.

But Thad's trained enlisted personnel, his horses and wagons, even his commander, General Humphries, all had been dispersed to other duties. Nevertheless, the corps managed to render service throughout the fall, at Harper's Ferry and Fredericksburg. Balloon reconnaissance had to be requested by individual generals, since Thad still had no authority to issue orders for his own department.

On December 22nd, 1862, the Aeronautic Corps was made an official branch of the Army. Thad was given the honorary title of Colonel, but nothing, in fact, was changed. The corps wintered that year with the army at Fredericksburg, at the request of Joe Hooker, now in command.

During the winter, the War Department demanded a report of the balloon service and Secretary of War Stanton asked Thad to write a history of balloons in war.

On March 30th, 1863, the Aeronautic Department was declared a separate and distinct unit of the United States Army. Still Thad's commission was withheld and nothing was done to help him create a working corps again.

The final blow came on April 7th. The running of what corps remained, was again taken out of his hands.

The eager young martinet who took over decided to set up rigid rules for the "civil employees" connected with the balloon department. Among his first recommendations was a cut in pay for all, from Thad on down. Then he demanded the discharge of Thad's right-hand man, Clovis, and of John Dickinson, intimating that their employment was favoritism.

In a written protest, which amounted to resignation, Thad pointed out that he had originally refused $30 a day to work for $10—barely enough to support his family. Besides, he had used his own funds and equipment during the early months of the war, for which the government had never reimbursed him.

He concluded:

> All of the aeronauts have labored incessantly and never shrunk from duty or danger, and this despite the fact that we could claim no pension in case of accident or death. The two men in question have been constant in their service, attending faithfully to the management and care of the balloons and all supervisory details.
>
> If my services to the Army are worth only $6 per day, I should in honesty, refund the excess I have received for the past two years. This I cannot afford to do. Since I have given my word to General Hooker that I shall support him during the battle now impending, I shall remain throughout the emergency without compensation."

The battle was near Chancellorsville, Virginia. For five days, from April 30th through May 5th, the aeronauts were aloft night and day. When Thad descended for the last time, a sense of revulsion accompanied his fatigue. He had seen thousands of men killed or maimed for life. His own first commander, Amiel Whipple, now Major General, lay mortally wounded. Yet hardly an inch of ground had been won or lost by either side.

Thad had kept his word. Now he could go home.

The stately mountains encircled a peaceful oasis in a tortured land. From the wide veranda of Ben Plaisted's inn, the Waumbek, Thad looked down on the pine-scented valley of the Singrawac, and the memory of seared battlefields dissolved.

It was the end of August, when Thad's eldest stepbrother decided to honor the Lowes with a banquet. Vyron and Charles Edward caught 400 rainbow trout that day. They were prepared in the Waumbek's kitchen.

When all the Lowes, the sons and daughters, the uncles and cousins, the friends, and all the offspring, gathered in the Waumbek dining room, it looked as though most of Jefferson and half of Randolph were there.

"Never," Thad exclaimed appreciatively, "even as a boy, did I catch fish like that!"

After dinner, when the men gathered in the parlor for their brandy and smokes, Clovis asked Thad outright:

"Well, son, what's to be done about the balloon corps?"

The men knew that Thad had had letters from many of the generals under whom he had served, wishing him a speedy return to health—and to the Army. As the contest of arms between the states became more savage and bitter, newspapers across the country pressed for better military organization. A permanent aeronautic branch of the army was a favorite point.

Clovis knew that six superior silk balloons complete with generating equipment lay idle at the Columbian Armory in Washington. Even the Allen boys had finally given up and gone home to Providence.

He knew Thad had perfected an improved calcium light by which an army could construct bridges or breastworks, or carry on night operations while its rays remained hidden from the enemy. It had not even been given an official test. Nor had the varicolored phosphorescent signal balloons been employed, though Thad had found them to be more brilliant than a rocket and visible ten times as long.

There had never been an opportunity to have Matthew Brady try the magnifying lenses by which Thad hoped aerial photographs might be enlarged from three inches square to as much as twenty feet. Objects not discernible to the naked eye he thought might be distinguished in a picture thus enlarged.

Must all these valuable inventions await a more enlightened, less preoccupied generation? It appeared so, for Thad replied to his father's question in the negative.

"I submitted a report of my work and plans for a regular air corps to the War Department," Thad reminded him. "But Dr. Andrews' experience has made me certain they will not be acted upon in the foreseeable future."

During the summer, Dr. Solomon Andrews of New Jersey had flown a powered airship over New York City. He had offered to build such a ship for the Army, but Secretary of War Stanton declared he could not see its "practical utility" as the use of airpower was "too remote."

Thad shrugged his shoulders. "Actually, aeronautics cannot advance much more until a light but powerful engine is perfected. The aircraft of the future will be a sort of air sled, like a glider with a motor, requiring no balloon. It would ride the air like a bird."

Speculation as to the future of air transportation was interrupted by the invasion of a group of leggy youngsters.

"Tell again about the pretty balloon, Daddy," cried Thad's oldest daughter Louisa.

"Tell us again, Uncle Thad!" chorused the other children.

They were referring to the gay sky bauble that had been the one bright spot in Thad's grim last day beside the Chickahominy. Thad had told the children how he had watched the dazzling aircraft through his telescope from the porch at Malvern House while he was recuperating from the fever.

Apparently the Confederates inflated the balloon at Richmond and brought it to the scene of action by rail or steamer, down the James. One day its tug went aground while it was aloft from the deck. Balloon and carrier were seized by Federal gunboats.

The prisoners told how the gay balloon had been constructed. Confederate officers had watched with envy the Federal balloons, floating high in the air, well out of range of their guns. They felt their every move was observed.

"They tried a balloon made of cotton at Yorktown," Thad retold the story with relish, "but it hardly got off the ground it was so heavy. Yet there was no silk to be had in all the Confederate states!"

Thad's round-eyed audience sighed in unison. The story was a fairy tale to them.

"One day," Thad continued, "a man named Langdon Cheves from Savannah, Georgia, had an idea. Before the war, all the southern ladies had imported silk from abroad to make the gay party dresses they loved so well. All the frocks in the Confederacy, even wedding dresses, were gathered up to make a balloon. That is why it was called the "silk dress balloon."

Thad reached in his pocket and drew out a piece of colored silk. The pitiful scrap evoked in Thad a bitter memory—of everlasting rain and mud, of gunsmoke and blood, and of a million men who would never return from the stinking swamps beside the Chickahominy.

"It was too bad to cut it up in little pieces, Daddy." Louisa's sweet voice banished the horrid picture.

Thad had to agree. It was all too bad.

When the children had run out again to play, Charles Edward took his brother aside.

"Are you going to give up aeronautics entirely, Thad?" he asked.

"Not entirely, Charlie," said Thad. "But for serious scientific research, I must turn to other fields."

CHAPTER NINETEEN

THRESHOLD OF THE AGE OF FLIGHT

That autumn Thad settled his family on a small estate in the Valley Forge hills of Pennsylvania, near George Washington's historic headquarters.

He was already busy on plans for an artificial ice machine. The absorption of heat attendant on the vaporization of gas, when released from compression within his balloons, was the seed of his idea for a mechanical refrigeration system.

"Imagine the possibility of preserving fresh meats and vegetables in their natural state!" he enthused to Leontine. "No salting or drying, no dousing with vinegar! The real flavor could be retained. Nor need one be dependent on deep caves or root cellars or the fickleness of natural ice and snow. Southerners and city folk could have fresh foods all year round as well as the farmers up home."

To finance his research, Thad set up a balloon station in New York City's Central Park and advertised regular passenger air service to Atlantic City and other nearby points. Balloon trips proved a popular novelty, netting Thad a handsome income, but air travel was too chancy to be accepted as a regular mode of transportation.

On April 3, 1865, the armies of Ulysses S. Grant marched into flaming Richmond. Retreating Confederate defenders had fired their Capital in a last gesture of defiance. But within days, Confederate General Robert E. Lee surrendered his Army of Northern Virginia to the Federal leader. The war was virtually ended.

Thad experienced relief without joy when he heard the news. The hatred and bitterness that had almost torn the United States asunder were still festering. He wondered if the gaping wound could ever heal completely.

Desperate anger blazed again from the gun of a crazed secessionist, John Wilkes Booth, on the night of April 14th and Abraham Lincoln slumped forward in his seat at Ford's Theater in Washington. By morning he was dead.

An angered nation turned its newborn wrath on the already battered south. Thad's grief at the loss of his friend was boundless, but he turned in disgust from the vengeance Lincoln himself would have denounced.

On November 8th, 1865, Thad piloted the first aerial wedding journey to Mount Vernon, N. Y. Newspapers reported the unprecedented event with awe. One commented gravely:

"The sacred compact of Holy Matrimony was solemnized above the clouds, floating in mid-air, and in accordance with the laws of the Empire State."

On this happy note, Thad closed his aeronautic career, to turn his attention to scientific research.

Thad's perfected "Compression Ice Machine" marked the beginning of commercial cold storage. As he had predicted, his biggest market was in the South. He was engaged in supervising installations of the complicated mechanism when a tempting offer came his way.

On March 4th, 1867, he received a letter from Le Chevalier Cavalcomte d'Alququerque, Minister from Brazil. His Imperial Majesty, Pedro II of Brazil, wished to employ Professor Lowe's system of aeronautics in his war with Paraguay. Thad was offered a commission, $180 a month in gold, all expenses, plus a land grant if he chose to settle in Brazil.

Thad recommended the Allen brothers in his place and supervised the equipping of the expedition. Ezra Allen later wrote Thad that the balloon service was considered a priceless advantage by the Brazilian Army.

As the War Between the States began its march into history, personal memoirs written by leaders of both armies testified to the efficacy of aerial reconnaissance. Apparently the salute of iron hail that had greeted the balloons whenever they ascended had been a genuine sign of admiration.

Confederate General E. P. Alexander wrote: "I have never understood why the enemy abandoned the use of military balloons. Even if the observers never saw anything, they would have been worth all they cost for the annoyance and delay they caused us in trying to keep our movements out of their sight."

The paper described how easily Confederate guns forced the Federals to abandon signal posts in the tallest trees but could not drive the pesky balloons from the sky. General Alexander expressed utter amazement that, for the difference of a few dollars a day, the Union Army had been deprived of this valuable service.

To Thad the war was a thing of the past and the whole question of little consequence by now. His ice machine had proved so successful he decided to equip a steamship with refrigeration to transport fresh meat, vegetables, and fruit. In December the steamer, *William Tabor,* arrived in New York from Galveston, Texas, the meat and vegetables in its cold storage compartment as fresh as the day they were packed.

Thad purchased another ship, the *Agnes,* and formed a company. But the public remained skeptical of food left unpreserved over so long a period, and the company failed.

Undaunted, Thad turned his energies to another project that had been in the back of his mind since the war. He felt certain that the principles employed in his generating machines could be turned to commercial purposes.

In 1872, he perfected a water gas process destined to bring cheap light, heat, and cooking facilities to millions. He had developed, at the same time, an incandescent gas mantle that gave off a whiter, brighter light than the naked flame, and other appliances for cooking and heating. The water gas system remained in wide use until it was supplanted, in the 20th century, by electricity.

Thad was honored by the Benjamin Franklin Institute in Philadelphia for these inventions. A model of the Lowe water gas apparatus is still on display there. He was awarded three medals and a diploma, including the Elliot Cresson gold medal and the Grand Medal of Honor for the invention "held most useful to mankind."

"He had little more than reached middle life," a current periodical commented, "and it is warrantable to suppose that his speculative and fertile mind will grasp and produce other valuable inventions."

In 1888, Thad and Leontine moved to California with their four younger children: Augustine, Blanche, Thaddeus, and Edna. The four older children had married and settled in the East.

Thad's eyes were on the heavens again. The new home in Pasadena nestled at the foot of Mount Wilson in the Sierra Madre Mountains. Atop a nearby peak, Thad erected an astronomical observatory and built a cogwheel railway up to it. Gas engines, powered by water, carried visitors from all over the world up the steep slopes of Rubio Canyon to study the stars.

In 1890, one of Thad's earliest ambitions was fulfilled. The State of California named his peak "Mount Lowe."

In addition to the observatory, Thad became interested in a new coke oven system to produce gas and fuel. Two useful by-products emerged from his experiments.

Carbonite, a light substance similar to coal, proved an economical, highly efficient fuel. It was especially adaptable to seagoing, power driven ships since it took considerably less stowage space than the bulkier natural product.

Calcium carbide Thad discovered to be a source of acetylene gas, a much needed source of light for isolated residences and barns not served by regular gas mains. It came into wide use for illuminating lighthouses and buoys, and later the "horseless carriage."

In 1897, the knell was sounded for the aerostat. Salomon Auguste Andree with two companions took off with high hopes to free-balloon over the top of the world. They were never seen alive again.

The next year, Brazil's Alberto Santos-Dumont made a successful powered airship flight over Paris. The perfection of the light powerful engine Thad had pronounced essential to further aeronautical development ushered in the century of flight he had foreseen and worked toward many years too soon. Now the world was ready.

By 1900 the Wright brothers' glider experiments at Kitty Hawk were widely publicized. Across the world, in Germany, Thad's admirer from the Peninsula, Count Ferdinand von Zeppelin, flew his first dirigible across Lake Constance.

"There hasn't been such enthusiasm to fly since the

Montgolfieres got their clumsy contraption a few hundred feet in the air," Thad commented wryly.

The youngest Lowes, Zoe and Sobieski, brought up on tales of ballooning, were violently infected with the new disease.

"You could build a better airship than any of them, Dad," the young people insisted.

Thad would ruffle their hair and remind them he was an old man in his seventies. Yet his vigorous body and active mind belied his words. Though his luxuriant mustache and goatee were quite grey, and a black skull cap hid the loss of the thick black hair that had been the pride of his youth, Thad's dark eyes were bright behind their dignified pince-nez.

And they did turn again to the sky. He had seen the weather bureau, for which he and Professor Henry had laid the groundwork, made into a national institution. Refrigeration was coming into widespread use. But Thaddeus Lowe, even at 70, was not a man to turn his back on a new challenge.

He considered the horizontal gas bag of the Zeppelin airship clumsy and impractical. He thought its framework heavy, presenting too much surface to the wind. While admitting the long dirigible was spectacular, he felt its lifting power was small compared to its bulk.

Thad began working on plans for an airship with the traditional globular gas bag. He maintained that the vertical balloon strove by its very design to remain upright above the weight it carried. It required no framework to remain rigid, was never in danger of tilting.

As plans for his Planet Airship progressed, Thad became convinced it would revolutionize transportation. With the light, reliable, high-powered engine now available, Thad felt his ship might circle the globe in 30 days, explore polar regions without danger.

The Aerial Publishing Company of Los Angeles, who issued a booklet in March, 1910, describing the Lowe Planet Airship in detail, apparently agreed with its inventor. The loss of Zeppelin's dirigible *Deutschland* on its first passenger flight in June that same year spurred Thad on.

The work went slowly. Leontine's health was failing and Thad devoted himself to caring for his beloved companion of more than 50 years, whose mind and spirit remained as keen as his own.

Despite all his efforts, the woman whom he pronounced "the most constructive influence in my life" passed away in May, 1912.

Thad tried valiantly to fill the vacuum of his loneliness. He turned his full attention to perfecting the design for his airship, but without the encouraging presence of his plump little wife even this absorbing task lost some of its zest.

His young daughter, Zoe, who kept house for him, could only guess at the depth of his grief, for he spoke little about it. And the spacious house in Pasadena never lacked visitors seeking the stimulating company of the friendly scientist.

That Christmas, Thad made the long train journey across the continent to visit his children and grandchildren. Ten days after his return, he lay down on the couch in his workroom for his customary afternoon nap. Zoe found him there towards evening. He had embarked on his last flight, to join Leontine.

Thaddeus was 80 when he died on January 16th, 1913. It was the eve of the First World War, a war in which aerial observation balloons were widely used, a war when men fought, for the first time, high above the clouds in powered "air sleds."

Count Zeppelin's "clumsy" dirigible airships rained destruction from the skies on combatant and non-combatant alike. The age of flight brought with it an age of total war.

Thaddeus Lowe would have liked to see the perfected use of aerial reconnaissance he had pioneered more than 50 years before. At the same time, the scientist, whose ideal had been to preserve and enrich humanity, would have been shocked to see how air power spread the horror of war.

The Planet Airship never grew beyond the drawing board. Even as Thad studied over its design, it became outmoded.—Or did it? Success was inherent in Thad's nature. After all, his airship might have been the "better" one. No one has tried it—yet.

BIBLIOGRAPHY

GENERAL REFERENCE

AMERICAN AIRSHIP PIONEERS

Boynton, Carroll, *Ballooning for the Federals,* Vol. 5, #2, (reprinted from Sportsman Pilot, N. Y., Feb. 1931)

Paullin, Charles Oscar, *Early Use of Balloon in War,* Vol. 39, #969, (reprinted from United Service Magazine, London, Aug., 1909)

APPLETON'S CYCLOPEDIA OF AMERICAN BIOGRAPHY, D. Appleton & Co., N. Y., 1888

BATTLES AND LEADERS OF THE CIVIL WAR, Thomas Yoseloff, Inc., N. Y., 1956 (Compilation of writings by Union and Confederate officers based on *The Century War Series.*)

DICTIONARY OF AMERICAN BIOGRAPHY, Vol. II, p. 452-3

FUNK AND WAGNALLS UNIVERSAL STANDARD ENCYCLOPEDIA, Unicorn Press, New York, 1955

HISTORY OF COOS COUNTY, NEW HAMPSHIRE, W. A. Fergusson & Co., Syracuse, N. Y., 1888

PHOTOGRAPHIC HISTORY OF THE CIVIL WAR, Vol. 8, Review of Reviews Co., N. Y., 1911

(Miller, Francis Trevelyan, Editor-in-Chief)

BOOKS

Bruce, Robert V., *Lincoln and The Tools of War,* Bobbs, Merrill, New York-Indianapolis, 1956

Cross, George M., *Randolph Old And New,* Randolph, N. H., 1924

Curtis, N. M., *Bull Run To Chancellorsville,* G. P. Putnam, New York-London, 1906

Evans, G. C., *History of the Town of Jefferson, N. H. 1773-1927,* Granite State Press, Manchester, N. H., 1927

Gibbs-Smith, C. H., *History of Flying,* Fred A. Praeger, New York, 1954

Harper, Harry, *Evolution of the Flying Machine,* McKay, New York, 1931

Haydon, F. S., *Aeronautics in the Union and Confederate Armies,* Baltimore, 1941

Holbrook, Stewart, *Lost Men of American History,* McMillan Co., New York, 1946

Lowe, Thaddeus S. C., *The Airship City of New York,* Baker & Godwin, New York, 1859

Lowe, Thaddeus S. C., *My Balloons in Peace and War,* Unpub.

Milbank, Jeremiah, *First Century of Flight in America,* Princeton University Press, Princeton, N. J., 1943

Miller, Francis Trevelyan, *World in the Air,* G. P. Putnam, New York-London, 1930

Oehsner, Paul, *Sons of Science,* Henry Shuman, New York, 1949

Sandburg, Carl, *Storm Over the Land,* Harcourt, New York, 1939

Shippen, Katherine B., *Bridle for Pegasus,* Viking Press, New York, 1951

Townsend, George Alfred, *Yankee Reporter on the Road to Richmond* or *Rustics in Rebellion,* University of North Carolina Press, Chapel Hill, N. C., 1950

Wise, John, *A System of Aeronautics,* J. A. Speel, New York, 1850

Wise, John, *Through the Air,* Today Printing & Publishing Co., Philadelphia, 1873

MAGAZINES

American Historical Review, July, 1937
Squires, J. Duane, *Aeronautics in the Civil War*

American Legion Monthly, Army Quarterly, Gas Age

Harper's Weekly, Description and picture of airship *City of New York,* September 24, 1859, Vol. 3, P. 609-612
June, 1900 (Article by General A. W. Greeley, former Chief of the Signal Service)

Leslie's, November 12, 1859, Vol. 8

Scientific American
Description of The City of New York, September 24, 1859. Vol. 1, P. 202
Letter from Battlefield, Vol. 5, P. 373

PAMPHLET

Latest Developments in Aerial Navigation, Lowe's Planet Airship, Aerial Publishing Co., Los Angeles, California, March 7, 1910

NEWSPAPERS

Cincinnati Commercial, Cincinnati, Ohio, April, 1861

Cincinnati Times, Cincinnati, Ohio, April 20, 27, 1861

New York Times, New York, N. Y., October 25, 1859

New York Post, New York, N. Y., November 11, 1859

New York Sun, New York, N. Y., April 13-15, 1844; October 28, 1859; October 31, 1865; December 21, 1868
Philadelphia Inquirer, Philadelphia, Pa., June 30, 1860; July, August, September, 1860
Philadelphia Press, May, 1898
Ottawa Citizen, Ottawa, Ontario, Canada, September 1, 1858

INDEX